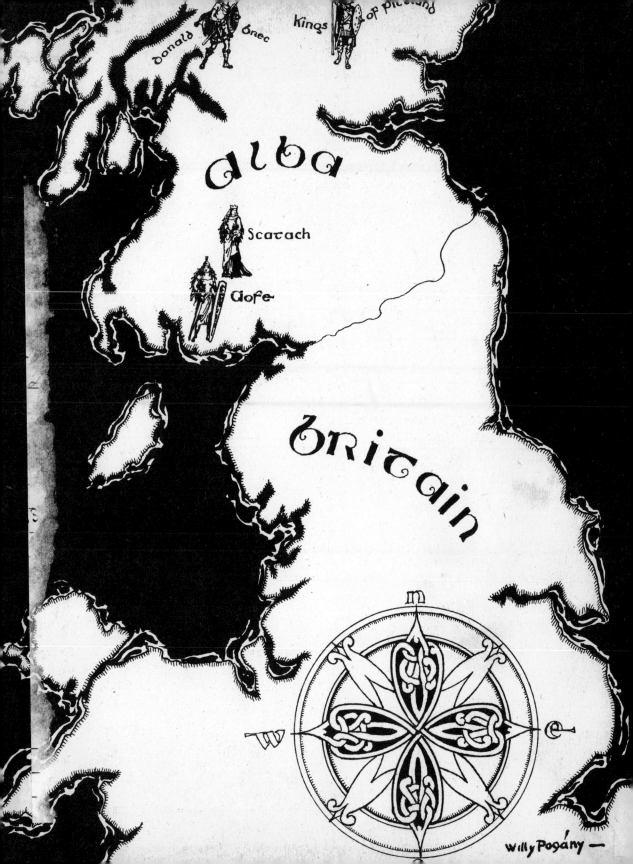

THE FRENZIED PRINCE

THE FRENZIED PRINCE BEING HEROIC STORIES OF ANCIENT IRELAND

Told by PÁDRAIC COLUM
Illustrated by WILLY POGÁNY

DAVID McKAY COMPANY

WASHINGTON SQUARE   PHILADELPHIA

j398.2
C72fr
cop. 1

To my old friend

JACK B. YEATS

who has painted the *heroic* in the *modern*.

Contents

Ind ráith i comair in dairfhedo,
Ba Bruidgi, ba Cathail,
Ba Aedo, ba Aillello,
Ba Conaing, ba Cuilíni,
Ocus ba Maile Dúin:
Ind ráith dar éis caích ar uáir,
Ocus ind ríg foait i n-úir.

The fort over against the oakwood,
It was Bruidge's, it was Cahill's,
It was Aed's, it was Aillil's,
It was Conaing's, it was Cuiline's,
It was Mael Duin's:
The fort remains after each in turn,
And the kings sleep in the ground.

translated by KUNO MEYER.

PART ONE

Prince Suivné and King Donald's Storytellers

AFTER A CERTAIN EVENT, to be precise, the battle of Moy Rah*, Suivné, Prince of Dal Arahee, was seen no more by kinsmen nor followers. But although he disappeared from the camps, the fairs, and then the assemblies that were frequented by the nobles of Ireland, it was known that he was still alive.

For there was an occasion when a man, whose appearance reminded itinerant persons of the Prince of Dal Arahee's, came to a settlement that clerics had made on the banks of the Shannon. Women were scutching flax and an attendant was ringing a bell for vespers. And this man said, "Even as the women beat the flax so my folk were beaten by Donald's army at Moy Rah." And again he said, "More accustomed am I to the crying of cuckoos on the banks of the Bann than to the *grig-graig* of the cleric's bell." And saying this the man, although a bitter wind was blowing and he was all in rags, fled away.

As he ran on he took such leaps into the air as made his going seem like the flight of a bird. "It was in such a manner that Suivné fled from the battle of Moy Rah," the itinerant persons told the abbot, "and since that time he has found his resting places in the tops of trees."

* Magh Rath: the battle was fought A.D. 637.

10

Now on a day that was its anniversary, the one who had won the battle of Moy Rah, Donald, the King of Ireland, came into Glen Earcain with a hunting party. Halting under a great yew tree he began to speak of Moy Rah. And when he told how grievous the memory of the battle was for him, there was none but knew he spoke honestly. King Donald had triumphed at Moy Rah, but the foster-son who opposed him, Prince Congal, who had been brought up in his household, had been left dead on the field.

"Prince Suivné of Dal Arahee, who was on Congal's side, was lost there too," said King Donald. "He was not found amongst the dead, and since that time he has not been seen amongst the living." There was a faint sound in the tree top: it was heard by Donald who was (as were all the descendants of Ainmiré) distinguished for his keenness of hearing. But he could not make out what it was: it sounded like a person's sigh. He spoke more about Suivné then, and recalled that the Abbot Ronan had put a curse on him before the battle. Then a voice from the top of the tree, a hollow voice it was, said these verses:

Men of the chase, stand back,   God has vouchsafed to me
O men from near my home!   A bare and narrow place;
Here, in the yew tree's top   No music nor no rest,
Is one who's wandered far!   Nor woman's company.

Here, straitened in the crotch
Is one whom God has changed:
His mind, his former shape
Are his no more, O men.

King Donald recognized the voice. He spoke to the man in the tree, naming him Suivné, and he pleaded with him to come down amongst them.

But the man would not do this. And when some of the huntsmen prepared to climb to where he was, he sprang from the yew to another tree, and to another tree from that, and as soon as his feet touched the ground he ran on, making such bounds and leaps that he rose high in the air. His garments were so tattered that they were like rags on a bush, and his beard and hair were like stacks the wind tosses. He ran out of their sight.

"Daft is the man who runs like that," said the huntsmen.

Later, as he went back to Dun na Nee, his stronghold, King Donald said, "Great were the ties that bound Congal to me before he made war upon me. I am troubled to find one of Congal's companions in such a state." He said this to the two storytellers who went with him, to the tall man, Colman MacAe, and the short man, Ae MacColman. And the storytellers knew that King Donald knew that it was his own policy that brought about the enmities that had led to Moy Rah, with its many slain, its great destructiveness, and the ending of the life of Congal Claen, his foster-son.

That night to a distant time did Colman MacAe and Ae MacColman go for stories to entertain the king, and the king's company. "There were other happenings in Ireland besides those that led to Moy Rah" was what they wanted to make known. And so to the time of King Fiachu, when the cattle on the ridges of Tara were all whitefaced, they went back for their tales. But Donald gave little heed to King Fiachu and the curious things of his time. His canopied bed with its gilded posts and its bronze rails gave him but broken sleep that night. Before the light of morning he sent for his storytellers.

The king's candle was lighted, and they saw their shadows on the wall, a long and a short shadow, when the pair came into the bedroom.

"I have had a dream," King Donald said, when his storytellers had wished him luck and prosperity. "In my dream I saw Suivné in a tree, in bushes and amongst rocks. He was listening to the unhuman sounds of wild places, to cries and howls. As he listened he grew more and more the wild man. And again I saw him, and he was listening to words that were spoken to him, and they who spoke to him were you,

Colman MacAe and Ae MacColman, and the words related the noble stories of our forefathers. They made a man of the wild man, for he no longer heard the howls and cries around him. It may be that my dream has shown a way to prevent Prince Suivné from going utterly from the ways of men. If you could discover what part of Ireland he may be in, I would have you go there and relate to him stories that would remind him of heroes and the ways of noted women, and remind him, too, of his own place amongst the descendants of Heber and Heremon."

They told him of a place to which the madmen of Ireland were drawn, and in which Prince Suivné, likely, would be found.

"Go to that place," King Donald said, and then he gave them this instruction:

"If you find him, relate to Prince Suivné your stories, dwelling particularly on passages that would remind him of his royalty and on the ways of life that our forefathers have shown us are the proper ways to follow. And there is another thing I would have you do. One who was steward to Suivné, Lynchehaun his name is, is now of my household; bring him with you."

Colman MacAe and Ae MacColman declared they would depart at noontime for the place they mentioned, bringing the steward with them. This they did. They found Lynchehaun helping King Donald's steward and claimed his company.

The place that the madmen of Ireland are drawn to, and congregate in, is Glen Bolcain, a narrow glen that has four gaps to the wind. In it are wells and streams with watercress and brooklime on their surfaces; there grow sorrels and garlic and many herbs. Back of it is a wood in which, besides acorns, are all kinds of berries; in the glen are rocks with crevices in which the madmen find themselves resting-places.

Prince Suivné was in the glen, for Lynchehaun found his footsteps on the edge of a pool at which he was wont to gather watercress. But they had no sight of him that day. The seekers built a bothie; and as they built it, strange, wild figures standing behind trees watched their work. They fled when one took a step towards one or another of them.

The next day Ae MacColman and Lynchehaun went through the glen, leaving Colman MacAe, the tall storyteller, to thatch the roof of the bothie. He did this, and then, being tired, went within and lay on a bed of branches.

As he lay there with his mantle wrapped round his head, a man came within. He was in rags and his skin was scraped with thorns. Seeing him lie by the wall, he took Colman MacAe for someone's henchman, and, standing by the doorway, he said these verses:

It is well for the henchman there!   I, who was once the wise
The one by the wall can sleep.   Suivné, had my lodge
Since the day of Moy Rah's fight   Upon a chosen site:
My sleep is lost to me.   Now I have changed my home.

I live from hill to hill
Around the Glen of Yews;
Would, would I had been left
Where Congal Claen was laid!

This, then, was Prince Suivné! He stood in rags at the door, a shake in his knees, turning his head towards where a raven croaked on a tree.

In a quiet voice Colman MacAe spoke to him. "There were battles in Ireland before Moy Rah; there were kings in Ireland before King Donald," he said.

"Yours is no madman's voice," said the other.

"When I speak," said Colman MacAe, "I tell of things that happened before Prince Congal went into battle against King Donald."

"I hear the shouts that the armies on both sides raised; the roaring of herds of stags is like it."

"Leave the stags to roar on any mountain side they will, but come with me where King Eochu hunts near Tara."

14

Into the bothie Suivné came.

"Your voice is gentle," he said to Colman MacAe. "I have heard the cries of herons and the screeches of cormorants. I have heard the fall of waters and the clashing of great tree-branches. I am one for whom the flight of a wren is as frightening as the advance of an army, and for whom the blackbird makes only a sound of alarm."

"Consider that you have returned from hunting, and that your story-teller stands ready to ease your mind with stories of far-off times."

"You are a storyteller—I know that from your measured speech," Suivné said, and he came to the middle of the bothie.

Thereupon Colman MacAe came forward a few steps and said, "Prince, a king of Ireland went hunting one day. But I will name my story. It is: MIDIR AND ETAIN."

15

Midir and Etain

THE KING OF IRELAND, hunting, rode through Bri Lei: there was a pool at the edge of the forest; before it the King and his attendants halted. What they saw was neither a doe nor a fawn, but a strange, beautiful woman.

Before her was a silver basin ornamented with four birds of gold. On her head was a comb of silver; her purple mantle was silver-fringed with a brooch of gold. Green, with golden patterns, was her dress, and across her breasts were clasps of gold. The sun that shone on the pool and that gleamed on the leaves of the forest made resplendent the green of her dress and the gold of her ornaments. His attendants whispered together, then one came beside the King and said:

"Your nobles have urged you to take a fitting wife, and your officers even now are going through Ireland north and south, east and west, to find such a one for you. Take this woman! None that your officers may find can be so fair or so noble as she."

The King (Eochu was his name) looked on the woman without a movement of head or hand or eye. She unclasped her mantle and took her tresses of hair in her hands ready to wash them in the silver basin. The two tresses of hair that she drew down had the gold of summer flowers. Through the short sleeves of her smock came her arms; her hands were white as one night's snow; dark were the brows above her blue eyes; her lips were red as rowan berries; her shoulders were smooth and as white as the foam of the wave.

16

"I would," Eochu said, "leave all the world's women for her sake."

She saw the King and his attendants but no fear showed in the face she turned towards them. A radiance like the moon's was on her face.

Eochu went to her, and spoke to her, and told her of his longing, and she said,

"I will go with thee. But thou must take me in all honor, laying a bride-price beside me, and granting me my requests."

"All shall be as you ask," said Eochu. "And what request would you have me grant?"

"That I never be made mindful of where I was before this hour," she said.

"What name shall we know thee by?" asked Eochu.

"Etain," she told him.

And so was heard that name that came into proverbs afterwards. For people would say 'Fair as Etain is she,' 'Shapely as Etain,' 'Dear as Etain.'

Eochu took her to his royal seat of Tara. Soon afterwards the princes and nobles came to the festival that it was the custom of the Kings of Ireland to give, the Winter Festival of Tara. Amongst the princes was Eochu's brother, Ailill.

When Ailill saw the strange, beautiful woman at his brother's side he became as one who falls into a dream. His wife laid her hand on his arm. "Ailill," she said, "why dost thou keep gazing far off from thee?" Ailill, becoming ashamed, looked no more on Etain during the whole of the festival that lasts from the fortnight before to the fortnight after November day.

The festival was happy for Eochu and his wife and the days before them looked happy. Still, one thing troubled the King. His brother had fallen into a sickness that no physician could understand. Now the King of Ireland had to make the circuit of Ireland. But before he started out Eochu spoke to his loved Etain.

"Deal kindly with Ailill while I am away," he said. "Treat him as if he were thine own brother. Do all for him that might bring about his cure. But if he should die, raise a pillar-stone above him and have his name inscribed in Ogham."

And so Eochu and his attendants went from Tara in their chariots.

The next day Etain went into the house that Ailill lay in. She stayed beside his bed and she said to him, "What is it that ails thee? Thy sickness is great."

Ailill did not answer and she sang a lay to soothe him. And again she asked, "What can I do to help to cure thee, Ailill?"

"One thing would cure me," Ailill answered. "If thou, Etain, would say to me 'I will keep tryst with thee, Ailill,' and keep it."

Etain kept silent for a while. Then she said, "I will keep tryst with thee, Ailill. Come at daybreak, forgetting thy sickness, to the house that is outside the fortress."

Then she left him and Ailill lay there with shame added to his sickness, shame that he had asked his brother's wife to keep tryst with him. But he would rise and go to the house outside the fortress at daybreak; seeing Etain there and speaking with her, feeling that she had granted him the meeting, some new life, he thought, would come to him.

Night came; Ailill lay without sleep. But just before daybreak sleep came on him; heavily he lay on his bed.

As for Etain, she went before daybreak into the house outside the fortress. Looking out, she saw a man coming towards the house, and, though he walked as if he had risen off a bed of sickness, she knew he

18

was not Ailill. She barred the door, and when she looked out again she did not see the man. In the course of the day she visited Ailill and as a man doubly shamed he told her of the heavy sleep he had fallen into. She would wait for him again, she told him.

Again Ailill lay awake until just before daybreak, and again he fell into a heavy sleep.

And, as before, Etain went into the house outside the fortress and waited for him, and as before she saw a man coming towards the house who was not Ailill. She did not bar the door; she let the man come in.

"One, certainly, I came here to meet," she said. "But from him who should have come I do not desire love; neither from him do I fear harm. And as I would heal him it is not unbecoming that I should make a tryst with him."

"It is more fitting that thou shouldst keep a tryst with me," he said.

"Why so?"

"Because when thou wert the daughter of Echrad of the Fairy Mounds, I was thy comrade."

"What is thy name?" Etain asked.

"Midir is my name; like thyself, I am of the Danaan folk who live in the mounds."

"And what made thee part from me, if it is as thou sayst?"

"The sorcery of Fummach; the spells of Breasal, put us apart." And then Midir said to Etain, "Wilt thou come with me, Befind?"

"Nay," said Etain, "I will not exchange the King of Ireland for a man whose kindred and lineage are unknown to me."

"Thou wilt be brought from thy forgetfulness," said Midir. "It was I who filled Ailill with love for thee; it was I who prevented his coming here to you."

But Etain said no more to him and Midir went away from the place. And then she saw coming towards the house a man who was certainly Ailill. As she went towards him in the bright morning she saw that he was hale and well. "I am cured of my illness and thou are unhurt in thine honor," he said to her.

And then they parted.

That day Eochu returned. He rejoiced that his brother was healed, and he thanked Etain for being gracious to Ailill. Etain was happy that Eochu was with her. She rejoiced in being the wife of the King of Ireland and she had no memory of the life that Midir had spoken to her about.

Now as for the King, he rose on the morning of a summer's day and he went upon the rampart and looked across the plain of Tara. It was beautiful with the golden blossom of the furze, the white of the haw-thorns, the flowers in the deep grass. When he turned from the prospect he saw a warrior beside him. The gate had not been opened. But there stood the warrior in a purple tunic, with a white shield that had gems on it, with golden-yellow hair and with eyes of exceeding brightness.

"Welcome I give," said Eochu, "to the hero unknown."

"I expected no less from thee," said the warrior.

"What name shall we know thee by?"

"I am Midir of Bri Lei. I know that thou are skilful at chess."

"I am skilful at that game."

"I would test thy skill."

"Nay," said the King, "the Queen is still in her apartment and my chess-board is kept there."

"I have a chess-board with me," said Midir, "which I believe you will find is not inferior to thine."

Out of a bag of woven brazen chains that he carried he took out a chess-board. The board was of silver and the pieces were of gold. He laid it on a pillar-stone and the King and he began to play. "I stake," said Midir, "fifty steeds that are spirited and strong."

Fifty of his own steeds the King staked.

Victory was with Eochu. Midir went from him.

On Tara's green next day there were fifty steeds whose color was dark-grey with heads of chestnut color; their chests were broad, their ears stood high, their nostrils were wide, their hoofs slender. They were spirited and eager but the rein stopped them easily in their courses.

But Eochu did not have these steeds well tended. Instead he had them yoked to carts and ploughs and had them used to clear grounds and build a causeway across the bog of Lamrach.

At sunset, as he spoke to his steward, Eochu saw standing beside the worn steeds the man from whom he had won them. Ill-favored was the face that Midir turned to Eochu. "Cruel and senseless is what you have done," he said to the King. And he spoke to the steeds and said:

> "Weary are ye, and your glances slant,
> One woman's winning this toil shall gain.
> Stones ye have cleared from Lamrach's ground.
> Whose shall the gain or the harm be?"

"We will play another game," he said to Eochu.

"What stake shall it be this time?" asked Eochu.

"Whatever the winner may demand."

There and then they played chess, and this time Eochu lost the game.

"What dost thou demand?" he asked Midir.

"That I may hold Etain in my arms and obtain a kiss from her."

21

Eochu was silent for a while and then he said, "One month from this day come to Tara; the very thing that thou hast asked will be granted thee."

But though he said this he made all preparations to prevent its happening. On the day appointed for Midir, the King had the best champions of Ireland placed outside Tara, ring around ring. Inside he had his best warriors and his wisest councillors. For them Etain dispensed the banquet, pouring out the wine as was the duty of a queen.

And then, as though he had been admitted to a festivity, Midir was amongst them. His appearance always was bright but now it was resplendent. Silence came upon the King and Queen, the warriors and the councillors. Then Eochu, the King, spoke and bade him welcome.

But Midir said, "Welcome or no welcome, let that that was promised be given me."

"My mind is not made up on that matter," said Eochu.

"I am to hold Befind in my arms," said Midir. He gave her the name by which she was known in another world—*Befind, Bright-haired Woman*. And when he said it Etain blushed.

"Blush not," said Midir. "I have been seeking thee for a year with the richest treasures of Ireland.

"Until Eochu resign me to thee I shall grant thee nothing."

"I will not resign thee," Eochu said. "Nevertheless, he shall take thee in his arms upon the floor of this house of mine."

In his left hand Midir held his weapon. He went to her and put his right arm around Etain. Then suddenly Etain yielded to him and kissed him on the mouth.

The King rose up; his armed men rose with him, but even as they did Midir and Etain rose from where they stood.

Through the opening in the roof they went. All in the King's house ran without. They saw two swans circling round Tara.

Springing on swift horses Eochu and his men pursued them. They saw the swans above the mounds which afterwards men named the Mounds of the Bright-haired Woman but which then was named the Fairy Mounds of Femen, but when they came before the mounds the swans were to be seen no more.

Colman MacAe had about reached the end of the story when Ae MacColman with Lynchehaun came to the entrance of the bothie.

Suivné, making a turn like an otter, ran outside and away. But he did not go far. He stood under the tree that the raven croaked on. *"Words,"* he said, and coming back, "would you say more measured words to me?"

Colman MacAe told Ae MacColman to relate the story that succeeded the one he had told. Then, while Lynchehaun stood aside and wept to see his master looking so wild, so ragged, and so emaciated, the short storyteller told: THE COWHERDS' FOSTERLING.

The
Cowherds' Fosterling

LONELY MAN was Eterscel, King of Ireland. He had been forewarned not to marry one whose race was known, and so from early manhood to middle-age he had remained without a wife, a queen, a comrade. Now that he had reached middle-age his nobles began to say "an unmarried and childless king is but half a king; Eterscel must soon leave his kingship to another prince."

And still no wife was found for him, for of the women lovely enough to be his queen all belonged to races as well known as his own, and of the women whose race was unknown, all were squat, ill-favored, and without accomplishments that would fit them to be the wife of the King of Ireland. And so Eterscel hunted and played chess and remained a wifeless man.

It has not been told that before she was taken from him, Etain had borne a child to her mortal husband. When she grew into womanhood this child, the Young Etain, was married to a tributary king. Still Eochu waged war on the Fairy Mound; neglecting his kingship, neglecting, too, his daughter. It is about the child of this daughter, the child that was the last of the Danaan race to mingle with men, about her and King Eterscel, that this story is told.

After he had married the Young Etain, the lands of the tributary king were ravaged by flocks of birds; they destroyed the grain; they

25

did not leave even the roots of the grasses in the ground; this they did, not once, but three times. The people blamed this depredation upon the stranger-queen. "She is too beautiful for our good," they said. And when her child was born, "Double will be our misfortune with this child in the land," they said.

And fearing the insubordination of his people, the king ordered two of his thralls to take the child and leave her in a wilderness where she would never be seen or heard of again.

They took her into a wilderness. But she smiled at them so beautifully, and her blue eyes had such wonderful light in them, that the thralls could not bring themselves to abandon her. They were cowherds whose hut was at a distance from all other abodes; the infant they took to their hut.

Now these two were brothers; neither had ever had a wife; they had grown old on the pastures and moors, knowing much about cattle and little about men. Awkwardly and tenderly they tended the child, one staying with her while the other did double duty in the pastures. She grew up under their care. It became known there was a child in their hut, but the few people who came near had only glimpses of her. Still, Mes Buachalla, the Cowherds' Fosterling, was spoken of.

When Mes Buachalla came to the use of words her fosterers reminded each other of songs and stories they had known; each strove to remember more and more stories and songs, repeating them to little Mes Buachalla so that she might have more of speech than the words they said to each other and the words they said to her. Very quick she was; no sooner would they say a new word than she would say it back to them. She loved to gather words and, while still toddling on the floor, she would surprise her fosterers with the words she was able to use.

When she was grown out of childhood the cowherds took her to their sister so that she might have a woman for her guardian. This sister lived even farther away from the comings and goings of people than they did; Cronn was her name. When the cowherds, one or the other carrying Mes Buachalla on his back, came to where she lived they saw her at the door of her hut, a spindle in her hands. Cronn was short of body, with bandy legs and a dark rough skin; when she sat she was like the stump of an old tree. But her eyes were as quiet as forest pools: nothing disturbed her. Her hut was as quiet within as a nest in the reeds or at the top of a tree.

But her fosterers had to use all their persuasiveness to have Mes Buachalla stay in that house. When she had fallen asleep they left her there. It was a dark night then; a wind rose and buffetted them in one direction. Then they were before the Fairy Mound of Bri Lei; it was Sowin night when there might be comings and goings between the world of mortals and the other world.

A hand was laid on each of their arms and they were brought within the Mound that was lighted up. They saw beside them a princely looking youth. "Yonder is my house," he told them. "Bring a load of firewood there every day." He showed them where to fetch the firewood from and brought them where they could rest and eat.

They were fearful, these two mortals in the Fairy Mound: they would be missed from their herds, and if ever they got back they would be punished for leaving the king's cattle unpastured and unmilked. And they might never get back to where they could see their Mes Buachalla.

The first time they brought the firewood the princely youth said to them,

"You have a fosterling?"

"Yes," they said, "Mes Buachalla."

"Henceforth you shall not call her that name. Call her Esa."

The next day the princely youth said to them, "Now return. But take with you fruits of summer."

So they took primroses and sweet-tasting berries and went out of the Mound and into a world that was leafless and winter-stricken. They hurried to the cattle-sheds. The cattle were contented as if their cowherds had come as ordinarily, and the steward had no word of blame for them. Two nights and two days they had been in the Fairy Mound, and it was as if they had been the night in their hut! The cowherds had something to talk about in the pasture. They knew they had been away for longer than a night for in their hands were the blossoms and berries that would not be in this country for seasons to come.

They became the stewards of King Eterscel after this, for the territory of him who married the Young Etain was made part of the domain of the King of Ireland. The Young Etain was lost in a mist that rose suddenly. Her husband was taken captive by raiders from the sea.

But none of these happenings were made known to Esa.

In the spring her fosterers came to visit her and we e surprised to find how much she had grown. In the summer they car e again, and, as they set down the wild bees' honey and the basket of he n-poults' eggs they brought, they exclaimed at her growth.

After this visit Cronn taught Esa the use of the spindle. Through the long days of summer the girl spun wool. When there was no more spinning to be done Cronn took her through the woods to gather mosses that were to make dye for what the dwarf-woman wove and spun. Any who saw them then must have thought they were unearthly things, one tall and slender with bright hair, and the other stunted and rough-skinned,—'a Danaan princess attended by a Fomor woman,' they surely would have thought.

Cronn, the dwarf-woman, had wonderful ways of her own. She could sit in the wood or on a hillside and have birds, rabbits, and even hares come round her; often she and Esa had hares and rabbits in their laps as they fed them with leaves. Now the dwarf-woman taught the girl embroidery.

Esa was happy as she spun and dyed and embroidered. As she worked she sang the songs that she had heard from her fosterers. And then a day came when, going to a pool to gather watercress, she felt as if someone went with her: it was as if she had a companion she could not see. And this companion was finer than either of her two fosterers; though she did not see him, she talked to him as she went along silent places, telling him stories, singing him songs.

She learned to weave and then her day was spent before the loom. Her life and the dwarf-woman's life were hidden and undisturbed. Only now and again did people come near where they were. When they did, their coming was made known by the bark of a pet fox that Cronn kept; then Esa stayed hidden.

Once a year Cronn put all they had woven and spun, dyed and embroidered into a pack and trudged off to the king's steward, the pack on her back. In these days it was to Eterscel's steward that she took the things.

Thinking upon the king's name, Eterscel, Esa went to gather nuts in a dell, the pet fox going with her. It was noon when she got back to the hut. Somehow it looked disturbed as though Cronn's going away had done something to it. The pet fox dragged at her dress; she became afraid and ran off. Esa was good at wood-ways; she found the track that her fosterers went and came by, and hurried along it, knowing now by what she heard that prowlers were about.

At the end of the day, from a rise of ground, she saw a place she remembered. Yes, this was her fosterers' hut. She went within, and saw the same pitcher at the threshold, the same pot she remembered. When the cowherds came to their threshold they were filled with wonder to see in their hut a tall, bright-haired, bright-eyed girl.

The next day they wove a hut of wattles for her. They placed it away from the track that went to theirs, a round little hut with a low opening for door and no openings for windows: the light came through the roof that they left open.

There Esa lived. Cronn came to live with her brothers; the spinning, weaving and dyeing went on as it had gone on in Cronn's, Esa doing most of it.

Now Eterscel had a steward who was always eyeing the people, always trying to find out what they had and where they had it. The embroideries and the woven and dyed stuffs that the king's cowherds brought him amazed him more and more. Nothing so fine came from houses that had the most noted weavers, dyers and embroiderers in the king's domain. "It would be worth while finding out something about the cowherds and their sister," he thought. So he went towards where they lived. As he crossed the pasture he saw King Eterscel coming back from hunting. 'A wifeless and childless king is but half a king,'—he remembered that he had heard some of the nobles say that after an assembly.

This was the cowherds' hut, he knew. Yes, and over there was some other kind of place,—a hut of wattles. Maybe they hid there the tubs of butter and the rounds of cheese that they scraped from the produce of the king's herds. It was a steward's business to walk around and look into thralls' and tenants' doings! So he went to the wattled hut. A tree grew beside it; he climbed into its branches so that he could look into the hut.

What he saw held him fastened to the limb of the tree. For within was a girl more lovely than any king's daughter: like whin blossom was her hair, like rowan berries her lips, like gentian flowers her eyes. And making her still more lovely was the look she had, a look as if some dear companion was beside her. But no one else was there, and the girl sang to herself as she wove at the loom.

Not knowing how he got down the steward found himself on the ground. All that he could think of was that hidden in the hut of wattles was a girl fit to be the king's wife, a girl whose race was surely unknown, for if hers was a noted race she would not be with thralls. "Mes Buachalla!" He had once heard that name. He would tell the wifeless king about her. And then, as he turned from the hut he was surrounded by a flock of strangely crying birds. His power of speech went from him. All he could say was "Mes Buachalla, Mes Buachalla!" and he went on saying it. No matter who came near him he said, "Mes Buachalla."

It was thought that the king's steward had lost his senses. He was brought before King Eterscel to explain what his words signified. Still he could only say "Mes Buachalla, Mes Buachalla!"

"It must be," said King Eterscel, "that my cowherds' fosterling has done some mischief. Go and bring him to me," he said to some of his guards. It did not come into the king's mind that the fosterling was other than a lad.

Esa was in the wattled hut as the word was given. It was the time when she could not make herself believe that an unseen companion was with her. She was lonely as she sat on a heap of fern, the loom, threads half across it, before her. As she sat there she sang to herself the lonely song she had often heard Cronn sing as she worked her spindle:

> Lonely sound the wild swans flying—
> From the lakeside far they go,
> And our land's green hollows.
>
> O'er the water, lonely, goes the one unspoken:
> Oh, 'twill bring me grief on grief,
> E'er return ye, wild swans!
>
> Lonely sounds a music telling
> Love is like a flight to clouds;
> In their wing-beats is lamenting!
> My heart's love is gone!

She saw a shadow on the loom. Looking to the sky she saw a bird poised above, a bird greater than an eagle, glistening and mottled. Dropping down, the bird was on the ground beside her. The glistening and mottled skin with its wings, fell off; before her stood a princely looking youth.

And Esa knew he had been beside her before although she had not seen him.

He stayed with her through the hours of the day, telling her how he, a prince of the Danaan folk, loved her because she had so much of Danaan life, because no woman of the Fairy Mounds was as beautiful as she. And he told her that she would marry the king of Ireland, but that the child she would bear would be, not the king's child, but his.

32

And he told her that the race that had begun with Etain, the beloved of Midir the Proud, would end with that child, and that henceforth mortals and Danaan folk would not mingle together.

After this the cowherds' fosterling was brought before King Eterscel. He was playing chess, and when he looked and saw her he was as amazed as the guards had been when they lifted up the wall of wattles and saw who was hidden there. "Here is the one whose race is unknown," they said to the king.

"The loveliest of all," said King Eterscel.

And Esa saw gladness and love in his face as he took her hand.

"Mes Buachalla," he said, and then, "Well it is for me that I have waited for you so long."

And so it was that the cowherds' fosterling became the wife of the King of Ireland.

When this story was told, Suivné took bunches of berries that he had strung on his girdle and gave them as rewards to Colman MacAe and Ae MacColman. He saw Lynchehaun and recognized him. "My lad," he said.

Then Lynchehaun began about cattle and horses, talking to his master as a steward would, and as he talked he brought him again into the bothie and prevailed upon him to lie down on the bed of branches; he put his own mantle under his head. Then Lynchehaun went to where Colman MacAe and Ae MacColman were.

They cooked the perch and the trout that Lynchehaun and Ae MacColman had caught; they gathered herbs and roots to go on their platters.

And as they took their meal Lynchehaun proceeded to tell King Donald's storytellers the cause, or what he thought was the cause, of Prince Suivné's frenzy:

34

"The Abbot Ronan came to Moy Rah to make peace between King Donald and Congal Claen. He did not succeed in making peace. Then he asked that the armies cease from all attacks after the fall of night. The leaders gave him guarantees that there would be no more slaying nor wounding from the time the fighting ceased with the coming of darkness to the time they went into battle again with the light of day. The Abbot and the clerics were pleased they had got this guarantee, and so were the soldiers in the armies.

"But Suivné violated them. Afterwards, when he was marching into battle at the head of his troop he came upon the Abbot who was reading in his psalter. Perhaps he thought Ronan kept silence as a reproach to him. Anyway, he became furious: he hurled the spear he had in his hand at the Abbot's psalmist. Then he made another cast; this time it was at Ronan himself. But the spear turned and went up in the air, for it had struck the bell that the Abbot had fastened to his breast.

35

And thereupon Ronan proclaimed, 'As high as that shaft has gone, may you, Suivné, spring in the air, and may you go as high as a bird here and there.'

"No sooner had he gone into the battle than his breath became fast, his sight became distorted, his legs shook, the weapons fell from his hands. Suivné made a bound that took him high in the air. He made another and another bound and went outside the ranks of the fighters. And then he fled, and he fled so fast from Moy Rah that his feet hardly seemed to touch the ground.

"But we have found him and we have won him to us," Lynchehaun said, "and it will not be long until we have him back in his own stronghold."

Colman MacAe and Ae MacColman were satisfied with what they had accomplished; they would go with Prince Suivné and his steward to Dal Arahee, and thereafter get the rewards that King Donald would bestow upon them. Then, as they harkened to the barking of the foxes in the glen, Suivné came to the opening of the bothie, and said these verses:

Water of bright Glen Bolcain,
Birds I have listened to,
Streams that make a murmuring,
From you I will go.

Sheltering trees and hazels,
Nuts and sharp-tasting sloes
Closes of dark-leaved ivy—
I leave you one and all.

Though I was gently born,
Though I was nobly reared,
My food, my bed I sought here,
Glen Bolcain of the streams!

PART TWO

Prince Suivné and His Wife Eorann

AFTER THEY WERE OUT of Glen Bolcain and away from the mad people who intercepted them, Suivné went peaceably with his steward and the two storytellers. They crossed hills and for a day they were on a plain where there were many kinds of bright flowers. The next day they went through woods where there were great flocks of pigeons. On the third day they went where there were pasture fields and tilled fields with mills on many of the streams. Women turning querns by their doors would speak to them as they went by. The tall storyteller liked to discourse with people at doorways and would often bring their sayings into his recitals of the stories.

The short storyteller seldom listened to them. But he, Ae MacColman, would say, "The old woman coming up from the well is like Cuchullain's foster-mother," or "that hag is like one of Clan Calatin," or, "the girl in the doorway is like Esa, the cowherds' fosterling," and he would bring descriptions of such wayside people into his recitals. The tall storyteller used to say of the short one, "he was brought up

38

in a mill, and so he has never listened to anyone," and the short story-teller would say of the tall one, "he was brought up in a smithy, and so he never saw anyone." They were sisters' sons, King Donald's tall and short storytellers.

When they came to the borders of Dal Arahee, Lynchehaun went ahead to inform the nobles that Prince Suivné was coming amongst them. They were heartened to have that news. But Lynchehaun was not heartened by the news that was given him. Suivné's wife, the lovely Eorann, despairing of his return, had taken another husband. Eorann was now in Prince Guairé's house.

The principal nobles came to meet Suivné and to welcome him back to his territory and his lordship. He was brought where a steaming bath was prepared for him; leaches attended him; he was dressed in a smock of linen with a silken garment over it, and a purple-fringed mantle covering all. But when he was brought into his own house, Eorann was not there to welcome him. Suivné did not speak of her absence. He did not seem to remember his wife at all.

Days went by in Dal Arahee. The bridles jingled outside, but Suivné did not go to the chase with his nobles; the feast was given by one or another of them, but if he went to it, he sat in silence; others played chess, but he stayed moveless in his chair. The assembly of his people Suivné attended, but he seldom spoke a word in it.

"Every night there is silence in the hall where Prince Suivné sits," his sister said to Colman MacAe and Ae MacColman. "But it must not be so tonight. One or the other of you will have to tell a story that will make a stir in Suivné's mind."

King Donald's storytellers went into the hall of Dal Arahee. There was Suivné in his chair looking fixedly towards the fire, and there were the nobles who were present looking at Suivné mockingly or pityingly. With Ae MacColman behind him, Colman MacAe stood before Prince Suivné's chair; after wishing him and his people victory and prosperity, he told: CUCHULLAIN AND THE BATTLE-GODDESS.

39

Cuchullain
and
The Battle-Goddess

UCHULLAIN LAY ASLEEP in his own house and stronghold in Dun Imrigh. It was near dawn when there came across the plain, piercing the walls of the fortress, a terrible and unearthly cry. All of the household were awakened, all questioned each other, all were trembling and white-faced.

Cuchullain himself, lying in the east side of the house, was aroused so suddenly that he fell out of his bed like a sack. He sprang across his threshold hardly clad. The geese lying in the yard had been aroused, too; the ganders, their necks lifted, stood listening. Then, from the west side of the house, Emer, Cuchullain's wife came, bringing him raiment and weapons.

"That cry—whence did it come? What did it signify?" Cuchullain said to Emer.

"It was a fearful, an unearthly cry," she answered. "It portends misfortune to us."

"What kind of misfortune?"

"Separation between thee and me—the cry was terrible enough to signify that."

"I will go towards where the cry came from," said Cuchullain. He dressed and armed himself in the yard. The great gate of his house

40

and stronghold was opened for him, and he went out on the plain that was his own domain, the plain of Muirthevna. This was the border of the kingdom whose king, Concobar, Cuchullain served, the kingdom of Ulster. Any attack on Ulster from this side would have to be met by Cuchullain.

He went towards a river that divided his domain from a wilderness. As he went on the dawn spread, the sun rose. Nothing did Cuchullain sight but cattle and such birds as cranes and rooks as he went on. Then as he stood at the ford of the river and looked across he saw a bewildering sight.

Coming out of the mist were a man driving a cow and a woman in a chariot. They were outlandish, the cow, the man, the woman. As to the cow, there seemed to be more of her than of any cow Cuchullain had ever seen. The man who drove her carried a forked pole; he was big, bearded and shambling, and he wore a long reddish coat. But man and cow were likely figures compared to the horse, the chariot and the woman. She was garbed in crimson, in a cloak so full that it fell over the chariot and trailed the ground. Her face was large and white, and her bushy eyebrows stood out redly above her eyes. As to the chariot, it had only one shaft, and that shaft went through the horse's body so that the peg met the rein across the horse's forehead. And the horse had but a single leg, one in the middle of its body. It threw itself forward, pitching the chariot on.

Even though she was someone to gape at, Cuchullain turned from the woman in the chariot and addressed the man with the cow. "The cow does not seem pleased to be driven by you," he said.

"What is that to you, Cuchullain?" the woman shouted. "The cow does not belong to you nor to any of your hangers-on."

41

Willy Pogány —

"Oh, indeed," said Cuchullain. "Then I was mistaken in thinking that any cattle coming on this territory is in my lordship."

"The cow isn't on your territory yet," shouted the woman, "and when she is there you'll have nothing to say about her."

"What is your name?" said Cuchullain to the man with the cow.

"He is called Uargaesceo Luacharsceo," the woman shouted.

"It begins to be something of a name," said Cuchullain. "He is speechless, seemingly. And," said he, gathering himself for the effort, "I will have to address yourself. What is your wonderful name?"

She shouted and kept on shouting something very long. "It is Faemorbegbeoil . . ."

Cuchullain cut her short. "I am not a man used to being made game of by wild folk," he said.

"And would you know the name of my horse?" shouted the woman. "It is . . ."

But Cuchullain sprang into the chariot and laid the edge of his spear upon her head, pressing it where the hair parted. "Tell me who you are who would come out of the wilderness and into my domain."

"I'll have nothing to say to you while you menace me. Out of my chariot!" she shouted.

He sprang out of the chariot and stood between the wheels. The man had driven the cow across the ford and was now going swiftly forward. "Who are you?" he said to the woman.

"I am a poet, and the cow that the man drives is fee for a poem I made."

"Let us hear the poem."

She stood up in the chariot, her crimson cloak falling about her, taller and stranger than he had thought she was.

43

Harshly, bodingly, she repeated this beginning:

Rock, rock, my battle-car,   Sing me to madness, sword!
Plunge, ye war-maddened steeds,   Lord, thou, and only love
Spear, strike on shield and ring,   Of the head-shearing queen.

Then he knew who the red-browed, crimson-clad woman was: she was Morrigu, the Battle-goddess.

"I swear by the gods my people swear by," he said, "that you shall not cross this ford." He held horse and chariot at a standstill while the woman shouted fearful prophecies at him.

"You will battle in the middle of a ford; I foresee that. You will be at death-grips with a man who is as brave and enduring as yourself. Then I shall take the shape of an eel and make a coil around your feet."

"Then," said Cuchullain, "I shall bruise you against the green stone in the river bed." And to all the prophecies as to the war that would come and the combats he would be engaged in that Morrigu shouted at him, he made answer with threats against her. "And you shall not come," Cuchullain told her, "into my domain, into Concobar's kingdom of Ulster."

From where was the cow brought that now was being driven across Cuchullain's domain and far into Concobar's kingdom of Ulster? The Fairy Mound of Cruachan in Connacht was the place the cow was brought from. A mortal had gone into that Mound on Sowin when the ways between the world of the ever-living and the world of mortals are open. A woman of the Danaan folk befriended him there. Strange were the sights he had seen while out of our mortal world. The strangest of all the sights was this: every day, carried on the back of a blind man, a lame man would come to a well that was before a fortress.

"Is it still there?" the blind man would say as the one he carried, the lame man, would look down into the well. And the lame man would answer, *"It is indeed. Now let us go away."*

"Why is this done?" the mortal (his name was Nera) asked the woman who had befriended him.

"They go to look at a crown that is in the well," the Danaan woman told him, *"a crown of gold, the crown of Briun. It is one of the chief treasures of our Danaan folk."*

And so it was first told of to a mortal, this crown that was in the well, and if it had not been told about, this crown of Briun, the war that the rest of Ireland waged against Concobar's kingdom, the war for the Brown Bull of Cooley, would not have been.

For when Nera went back to the world of mortals he told the King and Queen of Connacht, Ailill and Maeve, about the treasure in the well. They broke into the Fairy Mound of Cruachan to possess themselves of the crown of Briun. Some say that treasure was taken by them and some say they could neither reach nor take it, but the storytellers of Ireland have to speak about it because the foray brought the Battle-goddess Morrigu into the Fairy Mound of Cruachan.

She took away a cow from the Danaan folk, because it had been foretold that a cow from a fairy mound brought to a great bull that was in Ulster would produce a calf that, when grown to his full strength, would be the cause of a war that would make gleeful the Battle-goddess.

Cuchullain, by might and main, held her chariot at a standstill. Suddenly it was not there. He stood in the middle of the ford and neither horse nor chariot nor woman was before him.

"It cannot be that Morrigu has taken herself away," he said to himself. And then from a tall pillar-stone a crow croaked at him. He knew the transformed Battle-goddess.

45

"When the calf of the cow that is gone from you is grown there will be war, and you more than any of the other heroes of Ulster will have to bear the brunt of it." Then Morrigu went winging away, and Cuchullain went on the track of the cow and her driver.

But rain fell; rain hid every moving thing from him. He saw cows but they were of his own herds; he saw no man driving a single cow. And then he was before his own house and stronghold. Emer, his wife, was at the gate; she spoke to him about the guests they had—Concobar's wife and Laery's wife and Conall's wife, the most noted of the ladies of Concobar's court.

"Since you went, a flock of birds came on the lake," said Emer. "They are the most beautiful that have ever been in this country. And of your comrades' wives, each desires to have a pair of the birds to sit on her shoulders."

"And what is that to me?" said Cuchullain, "I am not going bird-chasing today."

"No one is more skilful with the sling than you are, Cuchullain," said Emer.

"The unearthly cry we heard portended the coming of one whom I should follow," said Cuchullain.

Emer became pale when he said that. But for all her memory of the unearthly cry she answered, "Each of the ladies who is here claims that if her husband was near at hand he would get her a pair of these birds."

"Put any of them before me in bird-catching," said Cuchullain. "I do not care."

"Nevertheless it will shame us if the birds are not fetched for them since they are the guests of our house, Cuchullain."

"I swear," said Cuchullain, "that the women of Ulster put us into danger by their request. I must be after the one who goes with the cow from the Mound of Cruachan."

"The house is shamed in which guests are not given their desire," said Emer, and she hung her head.

Thereupon her husband went to the lake and looked on birds that were on the water. They were beautiful indeed. With his sling-shot he wounded each so that it flapped its wings on the water. He went into the lake and took the birds and brought them into the house. And to each of the women who were guests, the ladies of the court of Concobar, he gave a pair so that each had two birds on her shoulder. For his own wife, Emer, he had but a single bird.

"Thou hast done what is fitting," she told him, "for there is not one of these ladies but loves thee, none in whom thou hast no share. But for myself, none has any share in me but thee alone." Her voice had foreboding in it. And as Emer stood before him, the beautiful bird in her arms, Cuchullain in his mind heard the unearthly cry and saw the red-browed woman, Morrigu, in the middle of the ford.

Suivné's mind was stirred. When the story ended he wept: he could not but think of the one who had gone from his house, Eorann who was as lovely as Emer, and who, he had believed, loved him as Emer loved Cuchullain. He moved from his chair. The chess-board was brought to him and he played.

The next night when King Donald's storytellers came before him he spoke to them; he spoke in a low voice but he gave them a welcome. He asked one to tell him more about Cuchullain. Then Ae MacColman stood before his chair, and after wishing health and prosperity to him and to the people, he told: CUCHULLAIN AND THE WARRIOR WOMEN.

Cuchullain
and
The Warrior Women

HENCE CAME the Gae Bolga, the spear with which Cuchullain slew his friend Fardia at the Battle of the Ford, and, more direfully still, slew unknowingly his only son, Connla? When they tell of how and when the Gae Bolga was obtained, the storytellers of Ireland speak of Cuchullain's sojourn in Alba, that is, in Scotland.

The time had come for Cuchullain to learn special feats of arms: there was but one person who could teach him such feats, the warrior-woman Scathach, whose territory was in Alba. The best of the warrior youth of Ireland went to Scathach's camp, and Concobar, the King of Ulster and the head of the Red Branch heroes, declared the time had come for Cuchullain to add to his battle-lore the lore that Scathach could teach him.

So Cuchullain took ship for that side of Alba where women were the rulers. Where he landed was at a distance from Scathach's dun or stronghold. He was shown the way to it: it was across the Plain of Ill-luck.

Long he was crossing that plain and many hardships he met in crossing it. He saw a giant sharpening his teeth on a pillar-stone, and had to swim a river of ice to escape from him. Then he came to a narrow

48

path across the cliff-tops. While he was on this path he met a crone who was blind of the left eye.

Hobbling towards him, a staff in her hand, she called to him to get out of her way. There was no way for him to do this, except to hang over the cliff holding to the path by his hands. Rather than listen to the crone's railing he did so. And as he was hanging there the crone struck his hands with her iron-shod staff. Almost he fell down into the sea. But with his toes he dug into the crevices of the cliff. When she had gone on he scrambled up and caught and held the crone, threatening to pitch her down because of her villainy. She was not so blind and feeble after all, he saw.

"You would learn feats of arms from Scathach," she said. "Know that Scathach takes only youths who are brave and agile. She knew that one who wanted to learn from her was coming along this path and she sent me to make trial of him. And," she said, "if you were not agile and brave you would not reach her, for you would be now lying broken at the bottom of the cliff." She laughed, but Cuchullain snatched the staff from her and flung it into the sea. Then he forced her to tell him what other traps were set on the way.

Between the end of the cliff-path and Scathach's stronghold, she told him, was the Bridge of the Cliff. Each end of the bridge was low and its middle was high: when one stepped on one end the other would rise and throw him back. Unless a youth was very agile he could not accomplish the crossing of the bridge.

Cuchullain left the crone on the path of the cliff and went on. He came to the Bridge of the Cliff. He tried to cross and the far end rose up and flung him back. Three times he tried and three times he was flung back. Then a frenzy came on Cuchullain. He was roused to the

49

feat that is known as the salmon-leap. He flung himself on the high middle of the bridge. Before the other end raised itself he had sprung across it and on to the ground of Scathach's island. "Here is a youth who has achieved valor elsewhere," Scathach who was on the look-out said.

Then Cuchullain went to the stronghold and struck with the butt of his spear the heavy timber of the door.

Scathach's daughter, Uathach, who was within learning sweet speech from Wulfkin the Saxon, heard the hammering and said, "A most active lad is without." She went and unbarred the door, and when she saw him she became quiet and shy and had only the thought to serve him. It was she who brought him where Scathach, beside a great yew tree, was teaching her pupils feats of arms: there were youths from the different provinces of Ireland there besides youths from different parts of Alba and Britain. Pictish and Saxon as well as Gaelic were spoken by them. And amongst the youths was Fardia, the son of Daman, from the Domanian part of Ulster—Fardia who became Cuchullain's close friend and whom he was afterwards to slay.

Scathach taught the youths special feats:—the blade-feat, the spear-feat, the wheel-feat, the use of the scythed chariot. And every day when he came back from exercises beside the great yew tree, Scathach's daughter would have meat and ale for Cuchullain and would have the bath prepared for him.

Uathach was well-built and well-exercised, and could yoke a chariot and drive it into battle. But she was crop-headed, square-faced, and had eyes like bowls of jet. She did not know that there were women with looks more pleasing to men, for she had seen only those who were wind-bitten from being with the cattle on the hills or who were begrimed from being in the forge where weapons were beaten out. She loved Cuchullain from the time she saw him outside the door. Her mother had refused her to many, but she would have given her to Cuchullain, and that without any bride-gifts. But Cuchullain was but friendly to her; he did not admire, did not desire Uathach.

One thing, she thought, would win his favor—that was a gift of some weapon that a youthful warrior would be proud to own. She had heard of such a weapon; it was on another part of the island, the part that was ruled by the Princess Aefa who was often at war with Scathach. The weapon was a spear, and it was named the Gae Bolga. There were many accounts of the origin of this famous spear, but this was the one that had been told Uathach.

Once two sea-monsters had pursued each other up the shore of the island. One, Curruid, slew the other, Coinchenn, and went back to the depths of the sea. Out of the long twisted beam that was from the snout of the monster that had been left on the shore, Bolg, Aefa's artificer, had made the spear that was named the Gae Bolga. It was the weapon Uathach would bestow upon Cuchullain. For it she would give two creatures she had reared and that had long been her companions, two great hounds. Aefa wanted these hounds: her side of the island was often raided by pirates, and nothing was more dreaded by these raiders than the fierce hounds that would attack men wading from their boats.

From where they exercised, he and the other youths, Pant and Ur-Pant who were afterwards the twin-kings of Pictland, Cuchullain saw Uathach going off, the great hounds beside her.

"You will have to get your own meat and ale today, Cuchullain," Pant said to him.

"I will. Try can you pull that spear out of the yew tree."

51

"And your bath will not be ready for you when you go in."

"No. You will have to be very quick with the wheel-feat to avoid this cast." So Cuchullain and his friends talked as Uathach went towards Aefa's stronghold.

She got the Gae Bolga from Princess Aefa and brought it back. But even though she held what she had gone for, not joyous was her return to her mother's dun. For Uathach had seen a woman whose appearance made her know that she and all the women of her mother's kingdom were ill-favored—she had seen the Princess Aefa. And now she became either sullen or sorrowful when she talked with Cuchullain, for she thought that Aefa's face matched his.

She would tremble when he would say, "I miss your hounds, Uathach. Some day I will go into Aefa's territory and see them again," or "Are there wolves to hunt in Aefa's territory? I would go there and hunt with the hounds you gave her, Uathach." She gave the Gae Bolga to him. And although he spoke his wonder at the greatness of the gift, and thanked her, and praised her for her generosity over and over again, Uathach knew that Cuchullain was more entranced by the gift than by the one who made it.

And then Aefa began to be talked about by those around Scathach. She was holding back the tribute she should send. And then there was war, and Aefa was coming into Scathach's territory with chariots and men. Scathach made ready for battle, and the youths she was training joined her ranks. But the one who was best amongst them was not where her ranks were formed: Uathach, when she was serving him, put a drug in Cuchullain's ale, a drug that would keep a man sleeping for a night and a day. And when he had drunk the ale, Cuchullain lay down on the rushes in Scathach's hall.

He did not hear the trumpets sounding; he did not hear Scathach's brazen-throated crier calling the names of those who went into her battle-ranks; he did not hear the rattling of the chariots as the host went forward. He lay upon the rushes while Uathach, forgetting that a battle was at hand, leaned above him.

She was stabbed and stabbed again by the thought that his face matched Aefa's.

But the drug that would keep another asleep for a night and a day could not bind Cuchullain's spirit for long. In an hour he started from his sleep. He sprang up and put on his battle-dress, calling on Uathach to hand him his arms. She would not, saying that Scathach had ordered that he was not to go into the battle. He snatched up a shield and sword and dashed out of the stronghold.

He came up with the host as they were forming their battle line. Already two of Scathach's sons were engaged in combat with three of Aefa's warriors. Cuchullain heard Scathach groan: she feared that the two would be slain by Aefa's three, and that Aefa would single her out and fight with and slay her. He heard Scathach say, "If we could endanger the three things that Aefa cares for—her chariot, her horses, and her charioteer—we might draw her away from the battle!"

Cuchullain joined Scathach's sons; fighting together they overthrew Aefa's champions. Then he advanced to the centre of the battle. And there upon a hillock, directing the ranks, he saw one whom he knew was Aefa.

She was the most beautiful and the most commanding figure he had ever looked on, and she was commanding because of her beauty. From under her helmet fell a mass of red gold—her hair. Her face was pale and small and every feature was noble. Her eyes were like stars of blue.

So amazed was he at the sight of her that his arm weakened. She struck at him and cut the sword from his hand. He would have fallen from her next stroke if he had not remembered what Scathach had said. "Woe! Aefa's chariot, her two horses and her charioteer, have fallen into the glen!" he cried.

She turned at that, and Cuchullain sprang forward and caught her under her breasts. Throwing her across his shoulder he dashed away with her, carrying her as a porter's lead. He threw her on the ground, and wresting her sword from her stood above her.

"Life for life, warrior," said Aefa.

"If my three demands are granted," said Cuchullain.

"Even as you breathe them they are granted."

"Give hostages to Scathach so that you will never oppose her again."

"Hostages she shall have."

"Take me for thy consort. Bear a son to me."

"As thou askest it shall be."

She rose; she gave him the kisses a warrior gives to a warrior after they have fought. She had her trumpets sounded and her ranks withdrew from the field. To Scathach she gave the best of her youths for hostages, and she went back to her own territory.

As for Cuchullain, for a while longer he stayed in Scathach's stronghold, exercising with the other youths, learning new battle-feats by the yew tree. Scathach praised him, prophesying that his name would be known through the whole of Ireland and as far as Scotland. Uathach did not praise him nor prophesy good things for him. She made a rann in the Saxon language saying that the Gae Bolga would be wielded to his own misery, and that not once but often. In a bitter voice she chanted the rann as he went from Scathach's stronghold.

Then he was with Aefa; he loved her, and love for him grew in that strange woman who had cared only for her horses, her chariots, and her charioteer, and for her charioteer only for his skill. Cuchullain was not long in Aefa's territory before messages came from Concobar bidding him return to Emain Macha.

When he left, he told Aefa that if she bore a son she was to send him to him in Ireland—she was to send him when the arm-ring he left her would stay on the boy's arm. He told her to name him Connla and to let him know that he was not to tell his name or race to anyone. He knew that Scathach's daughter was prophesying woeful things, saying that misery would come to him because of his life with Aefa. But how could she or anyone know what misery was to come: With the Gae Bolga he slew Fardia. And afterwards he fought with a youth who would tell his name to no man and slew him with the Gae Bolga on the strand of Muirthevna. When he was dying he knew who the youth was. Taking him in his arms he brought him where the Red Branch companions were. "Here is my son for you, men of Ulster." And these were the most grievous words that ever passed Cuchullain's lips.

Prince Suivné was silent for a while after Ae MacColman had told this story. But he thanked the storyteller and then said as if speaking to himself:

"Great griefs can be borne because they have been borne, and those who tell of heroes show that a man can be equal to his grief."

The next day Suivné went to the assembly. He put on such garments as a Prince of Dal Arahee was wont to put on when going to the assembly of his nobles and his people. To be precise, he put on a thin shirt of silk; over it he put a well-woven tunic with a border that had small carbuncles sewn into it; by his left side he put a golden-hilted sword. And when his steward and the storytellers saw him in his dress

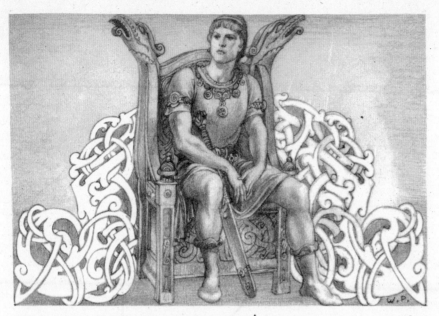

of state they could not but say that this was a different man from the wild, ragged person who came to gather watercress from the pool in Glen Bolcain.

As he took his seat one of the nobles said in a loud voice,

"I have not seen such royal attire since Prince Congal bestowed upon Suivné a dress of honor after he had slain Ailill Cedach in the first encounter of the battle of Moy Rah."

Suivné stood for some time as if he wanted to flee from the place of assembly. He looked about him and he saw King Donald's story-tellers who were present. He steadied himself; then he said,

"If any other battle took place that was likelier to cause frenzy than the battle of Moy Rah, I would fain hear of it."

The business of the assembly was halted.

Then Colman MacAe came to where the principal persons were, and after wishing prosperity to the prince and wisdom to the assembly, told: THE DEATH OF CUCHULLAIN.

57

The
Death of Cuchullain

AT LAST those evil magicians, the Clan Calatin, had shaped the things that might daunt, make doubtful of itself, and in the end, overthrow the heroism that guarded the land. Out of the flesh and bones of men slain by treachery, of women slain by violence, of children slain by hunger, they shaped a terrifying host. The champions of Ireland would lose their spirit when that host came before them. Then the heroism that was hateful to the Clan Calatin would go down. And the hero who above all others stood for the heroism of the land and whom above all others the Clan Calatin hated, namely Cuchullain, would be the first to be destroyed.

But the Clan Calatin knew that a hero cannot be destroyed by phantoms and by spells. He can be misled and his powers can be diminished by them, but only a weapon in a man's hand can reave his life from him. So the Clan Calatin went to men who hated Cuchullain because of destruction he had brought on their fathers and their people in former wars; to Erc, son of Cairbry, and to Lewy, son of Curoi, and they told them that if they assembled armies and invaded the province of Cuchullain's king they would lend them magic aid.

So it was that Erc and Lewy got their forces together and they went towards Muirthevna where Cuchullain dwelt in a stronghold that guarded the borders of Ulster.

Suddenly, before word could be brought to Emain Macha where Concobar, the Ulster King, and the other Ultonian heroes abode, the land was filled with flame and smoke. The smoke and flame was appearance only that went far in advance of the armies of Erc and Lewy and was caused by the sorceries of Clan Calatin. But when word of that appearance was brought to him, Cuchullain, although a man anguished by other griefs, ordered Laeg, his charioteer, to harness his steed, the Grey of Macha.

"I swear by the gods my people swear by," the charioteer answered, "that though all Concobar's army was pressing him, the Grey of Macha could not be got between the shafts of your chariot. And to you, Cuchullain, I say that though I have never yet refused a command of yours, the Grey of Macha I cannot handle."

Then Cuchullain went himself to where his wise, famous, well-tried steed was grazing, to bring him to the chariot. The Grey of Macha turned his left side to him not once, but twice, and three times. Then did Cuchullain reproach the steed that always had been ready to do his bidding. The Grey of Macha bent his head; great tears flowed from his eyes and fell at his master's feet. But Cuchullain led him to the chariot. Laeg yoked him and took the reins in his hands. Cuchullain armed himself with his sword and his spears and sprang into the chariot. And the thrice fifty queens who loved him knew what was happening, and as he sped from Muirthevna they raised a great cry.

The house of his foster-mother was on the way. Cuchullain never passed it without going within and taking a drink that she kept prepared for him. As he sat on the bench by her hearth his foster-mother spoke of his great deeds, how he alone had held back the armies of Queen Maeve when they invaded the province of Ulster, and how he had fought with and slain the friend of his bosom, Fardia, to protect that province, and how he had gone into the fortress of that giant king, Curoi, and had slain him there and had taken away his lovely captive, Blanaid. She reminded him of things that were unlucky for him to do: to eat from a strange cooking-hearth or to eat the flesh of the animal for whom he was named—Cuchullain, Culain's Hound.

Again, with Laeg driving the chariot, he sped towards where the smoke showed thickest, the flame most mounting. There came to him through it the wailing of women, the cries of youngsters beset with enemies, the battle-cries of warriors, the moaning of herds that were being driven away. He saw three crones by the roadside; they were at a cooking-hearth; on spits by the fire meat was roasting. Each crone was blind of the left eye and lame of the left leg.

"Visit us, O Cuchullain," they cried as his chariot came near them.

"It is not a time to visit you," Cuchullain answered.

"But if this was a great cooking-hearth you would visit us," said the crone. "Despicable are the great who cannot endure the lowly and the poor."

Then Cuchullain sprang from the chariot and went to the hearth. They gave him a spit with meat on it. As he took it he knew what meat it was—the flesh of a hound. He took it in his left hand, he put it under his left thigh. Thereupon his left hand, his left thigh lost a portion of their vigor. But his right hand and his right thigh the malice of the crones who were of the Clan Calatin did not injure.

Driven by Laeg, drawn by the Grey of Macha, his chariot dashed on.

In Cuchullain's hand the sword gleamed, the rays of valor were around his head, his hair falling across his forehead was like splashes of gold over the crucible of a cunning gold-smith.

And then before him was a host of frenzied, blood-stained, shrieking men and women. They seemed to be as many as the buttercups on the plain of Moy Brai on a day of summer. Their shrieking deafened Laeg and Cuchullain. The Grey of Macha swerved from them. Along Cuchullain's left arm and thigh a deadness came. From them came a breath or a blast that dulled so that the Grey of Macha shook between the chariot-shafts.

But Cuchullain, sword in hand dashed amongst them, cutting them down although their clammy touch made flesh creep and blood run cold. "None shall be left," he said to Laeg, "to daunt the heroes who will follow us."

Against others they would have been powerful, but against the bravery of Cuchullain's spirit the phantoms were not powerful. He went through them and they rose above him; like a mist they drifted from the place.

And now Cuchullain was before the armies that were falling into place, the army of Lewy on one side, the army of Erc on the other. As, the chariot halted, Cuchullain surveyed the armies, a man came to him, a Druid he was.

"A gift from thee to me, Cuchullain," he said.

"What gift?"

"A spear of thy three spears."

"I swear by the gods my people swear by that thou dost not need it more than I do. Erc's men and Lewy's men are before me and I have to battle with them."

"Then I shall revile thee because of thy niggardliness," said the Druid, "and hereafter for all time men will always remember my verses dispraising thee."

"I have never been reviled for niggardliness, nor churlishness," said Cuchullain, and with that he flung the spear, butt-end towards the Druid. It killed nine men in the ranks behind him.

The Druid picked up the spear. "A king will die by it today," he said.

The army of Erc and the army of Lewy joined; they linked their shields and made a strong and stern front against Cuchullain. He dashed against them; he plied his sword and his spear, and limbs and bodies were on the plain of Muirthevna. And when he had dashed the armies against each other, Cuchullain stood beside his chariot ready to battle again but hopeful that in a while the army of Concobar would threaten the armies before him. And as he stood there a Druid came to him.

"A gift from thee to me, Cuchullain!"

"What gift?"

"A spear of thy two spears."

"I am not bound to grant more than one request this day. Already I have paid for mine honor."

"For thine honor, but not for the honor of thy province. Unless thou givest me the spear I shall revile Ulster, and all men for all time will remember the verses I make."

"Never yet has my province been reviled because of my niggardliness or my churlishness. Little enough of life remains to me, and Ulster shall not be dispraised through fault of mine."

With that he cast the second spear towards the Druid, the butt-end before. Nine men behind him were killed by that cast.

But the Druid took up the spear. "A king will be slain by this spear," he said, and Erc and Lewy heard what he said.

If the army of Concobar was coming, there was still no sign of it. "Laeg, my friend," said Cuchullain, "we have only my sword and spear, your skill and daring, and the vigor of the Grey of Macha for the defense of Muirthevna. So let us go towards them."

Then as the armies of Erc and Lewy began their advance Laeg drove the chariot along their line, and Cuchullain, well shielded, cut down with his sword their foremost fighters.

Then Cuchullain drew away from the line of battle and Laeg gave him to drink from the vessel that his foster-mother left with them. A little while now, he said to Laeg, and the army of Concobar will be coming across the hill.

A Druid came before him. "A gift from thee to me, Cuchullain!"

"I have paid for my honor twice today," Cuchullain said.

"Unless I have a gift from thee I will revile thy race. All men for all time will remember the verses I make."

"My race shall never be defamed. Little of life remains to me, so ask what gift you would have."

"Thy spear, Cuchullain."

The last spear he had Cuchullain flung toward him, the butt-end before. Nine men in the ranks behind were slain by that cast.

"This is grace with wrath, Cuchullain," said the Druid as he took up the spear. "A king shall be slain with it," he said.

Then the three Druids with the three spears that were Cuchullain's went to Erc and to Lewy. Their armies stood, shields linked together as Cuchullain in his chariot dashed towards them. The eldest of the Druids who were the sons of Calatin flung the spear. It struck Laeg, Cuchullain's charioteer.

"Thou didst say that a king would fall by that spear," Erc said.

64

"It shall be as I said," answered the eldest Druid. "The King of the charioteers of Ireland falls by it."

"Bitterly I have been wounded," Laeg cried, and he dropped the reins and fell backward in the chariot.

"Farewell, Laeg, O my comrade," Cuchullain said, as he drove towards Erc's and Lewy's ranks. "In this battle I shall be charioteer and warrior also."

In spite of their linked shields he drove through the ranks, making a great gap in the line of the invaders.

"Fling thou the spear," said the second of the Druids to Erc, son of Cairbry. "Remember thy father's death and fling the spear."

Erc flung it and the spear pierced the Grey of Macha. Down Cuchullain's steed dropped, and Cuchullain himself, sword in hand, was flung from the chariot.

"A king, you said, would fall through the spear," said Erc.

"It is as I have said," said the second Druid, "the King of the chariot steeds of Ireland falls beneath it."

"Farewell, Grey of Macha whom I snatched from the immortal folk," cried Cuchullain. "Farewell, my comrade who bore me so wisely for so long." And, sword in hand, he cut his way through the ranks of the warriors and faced towards where Erc and Lewy and the Druids were standing.

"Take this spear," said the third of the Druids. "And as you fling it, remember Curoi's end."

And so Lewy took the spear and flung it at Cuchullain. The spear pierced him. Without his chariot, without his charioteer, without the Grey of Macha, Cuchullain leaned upon his shield and then drew the spear from his body.

"The King of the heroes of Ireland falls through that spear," the Druids who were the three sons of Calatin chanted together.

When Erc and Lewy came to him, Cuchullain said, "I would fain go as far as the loch to drink out of it."

"We give thee leave," said Erc and Lewy, "provided thou dost come back to us."

"I will call to you to come for me if I am not able to return," said Cuchullain.

Then tightening his girdle about him, Cuchullain went towards the loch. He drank of the water; he washed himself.

The armies of Erc and Lewy delayed to see what his purpose was. They would not get far into Muirthevna, Cuchullain thought, for now the army of Concobar must be on the way. Once more, single-handed, he had saved his province. "In my boyhood," Cuchullain told himself, "I swore by the gods that my people swear by that I would make my deeds be spoken of amongst the great deeds of heroes in their strength."

He saw a pillar-stone on the plain; he went to it and put his girdle around it so that he might be held upright, not seated and not lying down. Those who watched from the ranks of his foes saw that the rays that were the hero's light were still around his forehead. Then they were seen no more.

Lewy went to him. The sword that was in Cuchullain's hand fell and wounded Lewy's hand. Then with Cuchullain's sword, Lewy cut off Cuchullain's head.

But now the army of Concobar was coming near and the armies of Erc and Lewy drew back, Lewy taking with him the head of Cuchullain in his chariot.

And far in advance of Concobar's army, in the chariot drawn by his famous steed, Dewy Red, Conall Cearnach, Conall the Victorious, sped. A bond had been between him and Cuchullain: if he should be slain first, Cuchullain would avenge him, if Cuchullain should be slain first, he would avenge Cuchullain. As he sped on he came upon Cuchullain's chariot with Laeg dead beside it and he knew that his comrade had been slain. The headless body against the pillar-stone Conall Cearnach found; he went on the track of the chariot that went from it.

As for Lewy, when he came to the Liffey he went to bathe in it, ordering his charioteer to keep watch for him.

"A chariot is coming towards us," warned the charioteer. "Furiously it comes. The sods flung by the horse's hooves speckles the plain before him."

"That steed is none other than Dewy Red," said Lewy as he armed himself. "Unwelcome is the warrior who comes. Let him speed past. We desire not combat with him."

But Conall Cearnach did not speed past. He searched along the river's banks; he saw the chariot; he saw Lewy's charioteer. He called out, "I am one who claims a combat on account of the slaying of a comrade."

"He is a creditor whose claim must be met," said Lewy, and he went to Conall Cearnach. "I wish to have a warrior's pledge from thee," he said.

"What pledge?" Conall asked.

"That thou shouldst use only one hand against me seeing that this hand is wounded."

"It shall be as you ask," said Conall Cearnach. He submitted to his hand being bound behind him.

Then he and Lewy fought for two watches of the day and neither prevailed against the other. And then Dewy Red, Conall's steed, dashed at Lewy and tore him.

"Is this the pledge I have been given?" Lewy cried.

"I gave the pledge only on my own behalf," said Conall. "I could not give it for savage beasts and senseless things."

"Woe is me!" said Lewy. He sank down and Conall Cearnach's sword went through him.

"Take my head for Cuchullain's head," said Lewy. "Add my fame to thy fame and my realm to thy realm. I prefer that thou shouldst be known as the best hero in Ireland."

Conall took Lewy's head.

Now though the death of Cuchullain was avenged and though Conall and his friends dispersed the invaders, they would not enter Emain Macha in triumph until a week had passed. Cuchullain's body they buried beside the pillar-stone, but his head they laid in the earth of Tara, his shield covering it.

When the story was told, Prince Suivné said, "We, too, can fight against beings that bring terror." Thereupon he took his seat and attended to the business of the assembly.

The next day, following the wish of his nobles, he went to the chase. Now it happened that the chase went into a glen where Guairé, who had taken Suivné's wife, was already hunting. Eorann had accompanied him; a bothie was built for her, and she was resting in it when Suivné, dismounting from his horse, went to drink at a well that was there.

Looking up, he saw her at the opening of the bothie. He sank down in a swoon.

When he awakened he and Eorann were looking at each other across the well. Then Suivné said:

Once did you say, O Eorann dear,
A word that reached my soul:
It was that you would never live
A day from Suivné parted

Cold in Glen Awla were my beds,
Where I was man-forsaken,
A frenzied one, bare and uncouth,
Famine-wasted and wind-driven.

69

Eorann, stretching out her hands to him, said:

> Would I had been with you, far, far,
> E'en as a feathered thing,
> Not knowing where to rest nor eat,
> Out in the houseless wild.
>
> Would I had been where you went bare
> Out on the bleak hillsides,
> In coverts in the woods, or in
> The glens with waterfalls!

Tears fell from her eyes as she said these verses, and her hands reached out to Suivné's.

But with an uproar of hounds and shouting men, Guairé and his huntsmen came down the ravine. As he heard the din, Suivné fell a-trembling. He cried out that O'Faelain and his troop were coming against him in revenge for his slaying of Ailill Ceadach. He sprang in the air and bounded to the end of the glen. Then he ran so swiftly that he scarcely touched the grasses. And thus, for the second time, Prince Suivné fled from kinsmen and followers, a frenzied man.

PART THREE

Prince Suivné and the Madman of Britain

FARANNAN CLIFF is famous throughout Ireland. Over it a stream falls, making a sight that is pleasant to watch and a sound that is delightful to hear. On the beach below the cliff, seals flock; they come in from the main and lie on the beach or clamber into the caves. Behind Cliff Farannan is a glen through which the stream flows and in which are copses of hazel with nuts, apple-trees and blackberry-bushes. In the glen, too, are many hares and badgers. Altogether, it is a pleasant place for an encampment.

A synod of learned men assembled there, and Colman MacAe and Ae MacColman were in that assembly. They heard about two wild men who lived below the cliff, and it came into their minds that one of them might be Prince Suivné whom their master was still seeking tidings of. When the synod was over they went to the beach to look for the two wild men.

72

One of them was indeed Suivné. When he fled from Dal Arahee he wandered through Ireland, frightened by all who approached him. He came into Glen Farannan and lived on the fruits and berries and nuts that were plentiful in it; he rested under the thick ivy-bushes. Later he went down the side of the cliff and came on the beach. He lodged in a cave, and he had seabirds' eggs for his food.

He used to go amongst the seals on the beach; he would talk to them, and they, no longer startled by the sight of a man, would lift up their round heads and look at him with their man-like eyes when they heard the sound of his voice. To the seals he said this:

Many green trees are above,	Harmless up there were the hares,
And mast for the forest swine,	The badgers did not fright me;
Apple-trees with heavy fruit,	The stream that went on, clearly on
And bushes that hid me.	Made no noise to disturb me.

Suivné I am, once I was prince:
I can bear all but frost-bound nights.
The Abbot Ronan did a wrong
To me, O bright-eyed seals!

But a day came when he saw a man standing by the waterfall. Suivné was frightened, thinking he was one who had come in pursuit of him. But then, seeing he was naked except for a few rags, he knew him for a madman.

The stranger fled from him, but again came back to stand by the waterfall. In a few days this one came to know that Suivné was a madman, too, and did not flee from him.

So they came to be friends. Suivné shared with him the seabirds' eggs he gathered, and the other brought Suivné berries and fruits from the glen above. After a while they said to each other,

"He who first hears the cry of the heron, the screech of the cormorant, or the call of the plover as he rises from his rest, shall come and

73

tell the other of such alarms, so that we both may be watchful against men coming to take us."

Suivné named the man Fear Calli, Man of the Woods and named himself to him Fear Benn, Man of the Mountain. He bade Fear Calli tell him his history. Then the other madman said,

"I am a prince of Britain. Once upon a time two kings of the territory I lived in had a dispute. I went to the council of one of them, and I urged him to fight against the other for the sovereignty of Britain. On my urging the war was made. And I who had great influence in the land put the nobles under bonds not to go into battle except clothed in silks so that they might be conspicuous before all in pomp and pride. They went into battle. And even as the battle began the hosts on each side shouted maledictions upon me. A trembling came upon me and I fled from the field. I came to a storm-swept sea and found a boat and came over to this place. Since then I am a frightened man; I fear all who come near me except men who look and talk as madmen."

When he heard what Fear Calli related, a trembling came upon Suivné, and he said,

"Man! Man! It is my own story you have told. Listen! Ronan came to make peace between two who would strive for the sovereignty of Ireland, King Donald and Prince Congal. I made Congal go into the war and Ronan called down a malediction on me. When the hosts went into battle they uttered mighty shouts. Hearing the din they made a trembling came on me and I fled from Moy Rah. Ever since then the appearance of man has made me fearful. You are the only man I can let near me, Fear Calli."

Then Fear Calli said,

"You are the only man I can let near me, Fear Benn."

They kept together, but they gave each other no peace, for when Suivné came where the other stayed, he would say,

"I urged war on my king for the sovereignty of Britain," and Suivné would say, "Listen! Ronan came to make peace . . ." And whether one

74

stayed by the waterfall or the other went amongst the seals, he would have to listen to the story of what had brought madness upon Fear Benn or Fear Calli.

Then King Donald's storytellers came on the beach. They saw a man standing by the waterfall whom they did not know, but they saw another walking amongst the seals whom they knew to be Prince Suivné.

When he first saw them he would have fled from them into the sea. But they called out to him, "Tidings from Dal Arahee! Tidings from Dal Arahee!" and he let them approach him. He knew them for the storytellers who had come to him in Glen Bolcain, the storytellers whom he had listened to in his own hall and at the assembly of his people.

The next day, towards evening, he came to where they sat on the beach eating from bags of apples and nuts, and he brought the other, Fear Calli, with him. No sooner were salutations exchanged between the pair of madmen and the pair of storytellers than Fear Calli began,

"I was a Prince in Britain . . ."

Suivné said to the two well-clad men,

"For the love of Heaven, tell us one or two of your stories so that this man and I will have something to tell each other besides the happenings that put us in this state. If we had anything else to relate to each other we would, I think, be content in this place." Then rapidly he said, "Ronan came to make peace . . ."

A trembling came upon Fear Benn and upon Fear Calli, but Colman MacAe and Ae MacColman took each by the hand and made him sit down upon the stones.

And then Suivné said to the other madman,

"It is not your story nor my story that should be told now." And he said, "We would hear you, storytellers."

Thereupon, to the sound of the waterfall, Colman MacAe told:
HOW THE HARP CAME TO TARA.

75

How
The Harp Came to Tara

A TALL, FAIR, bright-haired youth: such was the one that Fiacal the robber saw when he went to the mouth of his cave. He recognized him. "Come up, Demna," the robber said. The youth climbed the ledge and came into the cave. There was a fire there and by its blaze Fiacal and his belongings were to be seen.

"What have you come for, Demna?" the robber said.

He had known this tall, fair, bright-haired youth before. With a band of boys he had captained he had taken refuge in his cave and had gone marauding with him.

"The spear Brigha—I have come for no less, Fiacal, my master."

"Take it, Demna."

"But will you let me have it just for my asking, Fiacal?"

"Long ago I got possession of that spear. Every year since then I thought I would use it, breaking into some Fairy Mound with it (for it is a magic spear) and carry off some beautiful queen or some great treasure. All the time I have kept it under the ashes of my hearth, the spear Brigha with its thirty rivets of Arabian gold. But you know how it is in this cave, Demna? The winds that blow through it would put pains in the bones of a wild goose. Now my back and arms are so bad that I can't lift the spear any more. I'm going to live with my sister's son who raises sheep. Take the spear, Demna."

76

"Bovmal the Druidess sent me for it. But I don't know why she wants it."

Fiacal looked at the youth. As he did, a thought that had come to him before came to him again: the thought that this youth was no castaway who had taken refuge in a robber's cave but one who belonged to some noted race.

"Who are you, Demna?" he asked.

"The foster-son of the King of Kerry."

"You never told me that, Demna."

"But hear now who I really am," said the tall, fair, bright-haired youth. "I am Cuhal's son."

When he said his father's name, Fiacal the robber gasped like a man who hears a voice come from a pillar-stone beside a grave. For no name in Ireland was more famous than that of Cuhal of the race of Bascina. Cuhal had been captain of a Fian—that is of a band of warriors who served a king of a territory. His was the Fian of the south, of Munster. And there was another Fian, the Fian of the west, of Connacht, captained by Morna. Now at that time a king, Conn of the Hundred Battalions, was spreading his power all over Ireland. He took the Fian of Connacht into his service, and between Conn and his captain Morna and great Cuhal a war was waged. At the battle of Cnucha, Cuhal was slain by Morna's son who lost an eye in the battle. Thereafter Morna's son whose name was Aed was known as Goll, that is, *the one-eyed*: Goll MacMorna.

All this was not so long ago although Conn of the Hundred Battalions had been succeeded by Art, his son, and Cormac of the Long Beard, Art's son and Conn's grandson, now ruled at Tara.

"No one knows that Cuhal left a son," said Fiacal in a whisper.

77

"No one knows because I was not born at the time Cuhal was slain by Goll MacMorna. My mother fled with an unborn child to take refuge in a forest on Slieve Bloom. Bovmal was her attendant. She reared me when my mother went away, for my mother, Muirna, married the King of Kerry. No, no one knew that Cuhal had left a son. If that had been known I, too, would have been slain. When I was grown I gathered a band of boys about me and went in search of those of my father's friends who were still alive. In an impassable place in the south I came to my Uncle Crimmal.

He was an old, old man and the men who were with him were old. They were weak and impoverished, too, and I and my band gathered some wealth for them. I heard from them the history of Clan Bascina and the high deeds of Cuhal, my father. Then I found the one who had betrayed Cuhal for the sake of the treasures that he, the Grey One of Luchra, had in his keeping, the treasures of my father's Fian that had been entrusted to him. Him I slew and I took to myself the treasures and the insignia. And then I came to you with my band and we went marauding with you."

"No one would ever think you had sheltered in my cave and had gone marauding with me," said old Fiacal.

"I was brought up by a druidess, a robber, and a poet," said Cuhal's son. "From the druidess I learnt how to take counsel from still pools and silent places, from the robber I learnt how to keep my own counsel, and from the poet, from Finecas, I learnt how to find words for my feelings and thoughts and how to give words a shape. I have lived with royalty, too—in Kerry with my mother's husband, the king. And now I am on my way to Tara to be one of King Cormac's guests for the Feast of Sowin."

"You cannot carry a spear on the way to the Feast of Sowin," said old Fiacal.

"Nor will I carry a spear on the way there," said Cuhal's son.

"And what will Cuhal's son do in Tara?"

"He will see who is to be seen there," said the youth harshly. "Unarmed, as everyone else, I shall go to the Feast of Sowin. It is at Bovmall's behest I come for the spear Brigha. She lives nearby, on a road to Tara. I visited her. And after I had taken her curds and whey she told me to come here and get the spear from you."

"And you shall have it, my heart's pulse," said Fiacal.

The youth went to the robber's hearth and took up the spear. From its head came a humming as from a swarm of angry bees. It was dangerous; it was a magic spear. And from its head came such chill that a trembling came on the one whom it was held towards. This was why Fiacal had kept it under the ashes of his hearth.

Out of the cave the youth went, the spear Brigha in his grasp. All was chill about him although there was sunlight on the fields. And a dread that he had to fight against seemed to get beside him. He was dispirited as he had never been before when he reached Bovmall's abode. It was a wattled hut with stones ringing it round and a rowan tree with clusters of scarlet berries growing beside it.

When he went within he did with the spear what Fiacal had done with it: he laid it with its head under the ashes of Bovmall's hearth. The druidess saw him do this but she did not speak to him; she seemed to be watching something that was far away.

At sunrise he went upon the road that Bovmall's hut was beside: it was one of the four roads that went to Tara. Where Cuhal's son stood he could view Cormac's seat in the light of the early morning. And he who had seen only wattled huts and straggling villages and single lime-white mansions on their mounds, gazed with delight on the splendour of Tara. For the grandson of Conn, Cuhal's son had no affection, yet as he looked on the roofs and walls and the palisade that ringed them, he thought that there was nobility in the one who had caused them to stand on the height that was Tara.

"Tomorrow morning we may not see them as we see them now," said the druidess who had come beside him.

"Do you mean that the roofs and turrets of Tara will not look so beautiful tomorrow morning?" Cuhal's son asked her.

The druidess drew down a bunch of the scarlet berries that were upon her rowan tree. "These show you," she said, "that we are in Sowin now, the first of winter. And in Sowin, the ways between the Fairy Mounds and the abodes of men are open. Men can go into the Fairy Mounds; folk from the Fairy Mounds can go into the world of men. And one of the Fairy Folk has a spite against King Cormac. Last Sowin he brought fire on the roofs and turrets of Tara, and this Sowin he will fire them again."

"One being, even though he come out of the Fairy Mound, cannot work destruction on a place guarded by a watchful troop," said Cuhal's son.

"Aillin can. He has fire and he has music. He plays upon his harp and the music he makes causes slumber to come on those who hear him play."

"If I kept watch I could keep awake."

"How?"

"A spear could do it."

"A spear, did you say?"

"Holding its point against my foot I could keep awake."

"A spear could do it—remember that, Cuhal's son," said the druidess. "But not any spear."

Then the youth went towards the high buildings that had roofs of red yew, that were faced with bronze and copper that shone in the sunlight. Conn of the Hundred Battalions had made himself king over the south as well as over the north of Ireland; his son, Art, had made Tara the royal place to which the lesser kings came with poets, musicians, historians and men of every art; Cormac the son of Art, Cormac of the Long Beard, had erected the most spacious buildings that had ever been in Ireland, and year after year had enriched and beautified them so that Tara shone as a jewel in the centre of Ireland.

Cuhal's son joined the brightly garmented throng that were on the way. He went as the foster-son of the king whose wife was Cuhal's widow. And thanks to his training by Finecas he had words and address that fitted him to companion nobles and men of learning. And there was Finecas himself! The old poet was overjoyed to come on the youth who had been his pupil, and very proudly he got Demna to repeat the poem he had made about the beginning of summer, May Day:

May-day! Supernal time!
The lovely colors stay,
And where there's shaft of light
The blackbird rounds his lay.

The cuckoo flies and calls,
That bird of dusty hue,
From branch and then from hedge,
'All, *May-time,* welcome you!'

Now like the raven's coat,
The bog is seen around,
The trout leaps in the stream;
Strong is the hero's bound.

And in the clear-skyed month
Man comes into his own;
The maiden in fair pride
Buds, and her beauty's known.

81

On us a longing comes
Horses to mount and ride,
And on the horses, too,
To take their mettled stride.

The water-flag is gold
Where shaft of light strikes down,
And up, above us all
A singing-fellow's gone.

The lark. And all are told
This is the season's prime,
Welcome, that songster shrills,
May-day, supernal time!

All admired and all were likely to repeat the poem when they got back to their different territories.

"But the best thing that a poet could teach a youth like yourself," said old Finecas, "is how to deal generously with men and women."

"I'll remember that you would teach me that," Cuhal's son answered.

They mounted the path that went up to the palisade. Guards in leathern jerkins and otter-skin caps showed those who were kingly or noble, learned or skilled, their several guest-houses. The foster-son of the King of Kerry was given a place with other youthful nobilities. Then came the banquet and Cuhal's son looked on King Cormac and on his captain, Goll MacMorna.

He had come to Tara to look on the man who had slain his father; he had come to mark him so that he might take vengeance on him. But now sitting in the banquetting-hall he did not feel vengeful. Perhaps this was because, while the Feast of Sowin was being held, no weapon was shown. Tara and all who were in Tara were very different from what Crimmal and Crimmal's old followers thought. And everything was different from what he himself had thought before he saw the shining roofs and tall turrets of Tara. He could not help but acknowledge that the one who sat at the head of the banquetting-hall, Cormac of the Long Beard, was a royal-looking man. And he had to acknowledge, too, that the one who, with his captains, sat at a table alongside Cormac's, Goll MacMorna, was not the ruffianly-looking fellow he had expected to see.

But for all the grandeur and glee of the feast there was trouble on the face of the king and trouble on the faces of men in different parts of the hall. And when the famous mead of Tara had circled around the tables, the king struck the silver chain that was across where he sat so that silence came on all. Then Cormac said,

"Our glee from the Feast of Sowin is lessened because of what happened on the night of the last feast and what may happen this night. As much of our halls and fortresses were destroyed as could be destroyed between midnight and daybreak, Tara will be guarded tonight as it was guarded on the last feast; it will be guarded by Goll MacMorna and the Fian of Ireland. We and our household will remain in Tara, but for our guests there are hostels outside the palisade."

It was then that Cuhal's son stood up. "All that an untried youth can do to guard Tara, I will do," he said. His voice was so ringing that to all present it seemed as if one who had the right to be heard had spoken. But at the table at which Goll MacMorna sat with his companions there was laughter.

"Who are you, youth?" King Cormac asked. "Where is your territory? What is your lineage?"

"I have no territory," said Cuhal's son, "but my lineage is from Bascina."

When he said that there were murmurs and movements in the hall. They had believed that the lineage of Bascina had ended with Cuhal.

83

"I am Cuhal's son!" Those bold words resounded through the hall, and then all saw that Goll MacMorna was up and was facing towards where the tall, fair, bright-haired youth was standing.

"I request the youth who has spoken to come to the king's seat." The voice that said the word, King Cormac's voice, had both gentleness and command in it.

He went up the banquetting-hall. Those at the tables saw how fair was his skin, how bright his hair, and they exclaimed "Finn!," meaning *the Fair*.

When he stood before him, Cormac of the Long Beard looked into his eyes. He saw they had steadiness, that they were the eyes of one who had faced danger. Here was one who was no falterer—Cormac, who was wont to judge men, saw that. But he could make clearer judgment of him when he had spoken, when he knew what was in the youth's mind. He said in that voice of his that had both gentleness and command, "If you help to save Tara from Aillin's fire, what reward will you claim?"

"That Cuhal's name and the race of Bascina be honored by you, O King."

It was a speech that might have cost the youth his life; Cormac admired him for having made it. Goll MacMorna rose in his seat, fire in that one eye of his.

"When the Feast of Sowin is over," he shouted, "I will let this youngster know that Cuhal's name cannot be flung as a challenge here."

"Nay, Goll," said Cormac, "make place for him at your table. He is a bold youth, and we may have him in the Fian yet. He might keep guard with you tonight."

Then Goll the Connachtman, who was as generous and as good-humoured as he was brave, made place for the youth at the table, and more of Tara's famous mead was passed around.

But as night came on, anxiety spread through the banquetting-hall. The guests were conducted to their hostels. The king rose, and having spoken with Goll, went away. Then, followed by his captains, Goll went where weapons were kept. He and the picked men of the Fian took spears and swords. Speaking gruffly he said to the one who was known as Finn,

"Take a spear, youngster, but remain away from us. If you will watch, watch by yourself. Find a clump of bushes and stay behind it."

This spear, the point pressed against his foot, might keep him wakeful while Aillin played music that made the guards of Tara sleep. And then he thought of a spear that gave out a humming noise like the murmur of an angry swarm, the spear Brigha. Its very coldness would keep him wakeful. And then he knew that Bovmall had wanted him to have the spear Brigha if he watched that night at Tara. For this she had sent him to Fiacal's cave. She had not told him to make use of the spear—no, because she wanted him to remember it as a hard-pressed captain in battle would remember the ford of a river through which he could bring men to fall upon an enemy.

Thinking this he ran towards Bovmall's hut. These were the stones that ringed it; here was the rowan tree. The door was open; the fire glowed on the hearth; no one living was there. But this was the spear, its head covered with the ashes of the hearth. Cuhal's son raised it.

He heard the loud humming that came from its head. Out of the hut he went. The chill came round him. He felt how friendless he was: no one would help him, no one would grieve if Goll MacMorna slew him. And what could he do against a power that was too strong for King Cormac and his Fian? Here was Tara, its turrets all dark—a king's seat, but a king's seat under a doom. He heard voices as men passed by the great gateways; he saw figures: Goll and his captains were keeping watch. He mounted towards the palisade. He saw guards here and there. "It's only the youngster they call Finn," he heard one say to another. From the spear he held came a chill and a feeling of dread.

Then he heard a sound. It was low, but it was a sound one had to listen to. It became louder, the music of a harp on which lulling notes were being played. As he listened Cuhal's son felt his thoughts sinking down as into a pool. The chill of the spear would keep him wakeful. He put the spear-head against his forehead. Nearer and nearer the music of the harp came; he heard its lulling sound, but no longer his thoughts sank as into a pool.

A figure came near; he held a harp; the music was made by him. He was running swiftly towards the palisade. And now he was above the gateways and walls, a figure that could rise in the air. By the fire that came from his mouth Cuhal's son saw him. He was blowing flames on the roofs. Fire rose from a building.

There were no shouts from the guards.

Cuhal's son ran to where the fire mounted. He saw by the fire blown from Aillin's mouth guards and men and women of the king's household huddled in slumber. Still playing Aillin swung towards another building.

Cuhal's son flung the spear Brigha.

There was a scream from Aillin; the harp fell from his hands. Aillin fell and crouched by a wall.

86

"Who are you? Who are you who cannot be lulled by my harp?" he asked in his strange, sweet voice.

"The holder of the spear Brigha," Cuhal's son answered.

He ran and lifted the spear and the harp. Aillin, grazed by the magic spear, was not able to make any upward flight. He ran swiftly down the hillside, but not more swiftly than Cuhal's son who pursued him carrying the spear and the harp. A moonlit way was before them: it was the way between the Fairy Mounds and the world of men and pursued and pursuer raced along it. Then the mound rose before them. Aillin leaped into its opening and Cuhal's son flung the spear after him.

On his way back he met three women wearing mantles of bright green. Their voices rose as he came near them, and this is what they chanted:

"Aillin has lost, has lost! His harp is taken into the world of men even though the spear Brigha has come back to us. Aillin has lost, has lost! Henceforth Tara will be unwasted by us."

Then Cuhal's son was back at the place he had guarded. Inside the palisades, and before the great doors the guard and the king's household were still in slumber. And there was Goll MacMorna, his great spear beside him, in deeper slumber than any of the others. Cuhal's son took up the spear and prodded him with it. He wakened, stood up, and looked around with his one eye.

"A turret is burning, but that is all," said Cuhal's son.

There was nothing for Goll MacMorna to do then but to go to King Cormac with some account of what had happened. He strode off, Cuhal's son going beside him, carrying the harp. And there was Cormac of the Long Beard walking on his lawn.

"Your guard must have been good," said he to Goll MacMorna, "for there was only a little blaze last night."

At that Goll MacMorna hung his head. "I slept," he said, "until Finn here wakened me."

"And you, Finn?" asked the king.

"I guarded Tara. Aillin I chased away, and the harp I hold is a pledge that none of the Fairy folk will attempt to waste Tara ever again."

"The tale you tell is strange," said Cormac, "but I believe it."

"By my father's wry neck," said Goll, "I believe it, too."

Cormac turned and walked apart. When he came back he laid a hand upon MacMorna and a hand upon MacCuhal.

"Shall I give Finn MacCuhal your place?" was what he said to his one-eyed captain.

"Was ever a king's captain asked such a question before?" shouted Goll MacMorna. And then he said in a very quiet voice. "I will serve under Finn MacCuhal!" And to make all this more of an astonishment he put out his hand and took the hand of the son of the man he had slain.

And Finn who really had learnt the poet's teaching took MacMorna's hand. "No matter what others say," he said, "it was in fair fight and it was to set up a king who could rule as a king."

King Cormac looked at the sky that was clear over Tara. "A new day has come," he said.

In token of that new day Finn MacCuhal put the figure of the harp on the banner of the Fian of Ireland. But it was on Finecas's counsel that he did this. He became the greatest captain that any Fian ever had. The only Fian known now to the storytellers is Finn's Fian, the

Fian of Ireland. He was a great captain because, in his own right he was a born leader of men.

And he had learned from a druidess, a robber, and a poet. From the druidess he learnt how to take counsel from still pools and silent places; from the robber he learnt how to keep his own counsel; he learnt from the poet how to find words for his feelings and thoughts and how to give the words a shape.

The storytellers left Fear Benn and Fear Calli on the beach and betook themselves to the glen. They had a bothie built there and the meat of a badger hung for cooking; there they took their supper and their rest. There was a new Prince of Dal Arahee, Guairé who had married Eorann, so there would be no gain in bringing Suivné back to his own territory. But they would try to bring him to Dun na Nee so that King Donald might know they had not failed in the mission he had given them a year and a day before. Then King Donald would give them the award he gave to those who did such missions for him— a ring of gold and a steed out of Britain to each. Suivné, they thought, would be so taken with their stories that he would go with them.

They went on the beach the next day and found the two wild men together. One held a nest of thrushes in his hand and the other fed the nestlings while the mother-bird flew about them.

When they saw the storytellers, the one who held it went and left the nest back in the ivy of the cliff. "Tell us one more story," he, Fear Calli, said.

And Fear Benn said, "We told each other what you told us and have kept in good spirits. If we had another of your stories we would be great company for one another."

Then, sitting under the ivy of the cliff, the storytellers and the wild men talked together for a while about Finn and about Tara, and then Ae MacColman in his pleasant voice told: THE GRUFF GILLIE.

90

The Gruff Gillie

IF ANYONE ASKED WHO was the best-looking and the most pleasant-spoken amongst the Fian, the answer was easy: he was Dermott O'Duivna. And if anyone asked who was the most unseemly and the most scurrilous-tongued in the three battalions, the answer, too, was easy: he was Conan Baldhead. It was a spectacle to see two such figures together, the handsome Dermott and the cross-eyed Conan.

But it was not when the white shields were against their shoulders and the helmets were on their heads that one beheld the unlikeness that made even the hounds and horses gaze and gaze. It was when, their nine months' service to the King of Ireland rendered, the Fian went to hunt the deer in Munster, making their camp at Knockany. They went there after the harvest month, the three battalions with their hounds, their horses, and their gillies. One year Finn appointed Conan the master of the camp and Dermott the starter of the chase.

When the baying of the full-grown hounds and the yelping of the whelps were filling the camp, Dermott came to Finn and told him that an uncouth-looking fellow was on his way towards them.

"If his looks don't belie his voice," said Finn, "he must be an outlandish kind of fellow." He said this because a big, bawling, brawling voice was now in their ears.

Into the camp came a shambling fellow leading a shambling horse. His chest was as wide as a door, and a pair of big, hairy knees appeared under his tunic; he was wide-mouth and gap-toothed and his head was as shaggy as a wolf's fell. An iron-mounted club was in his hand, and with it he struck the side of his horse making a sound that was like a wind tearing down a sail. The horse's ribs showed through its flea-bitten hide. It was a long horse, or, rather, a long mare, with a back like the ridge of a house. The Fian who were around thought that with every next blow of the iron-shod club she would be knocked over on the green.

And then the pair stood there, the halter on the ground, the iron-shod club held in one hand while with the other the fellow scratched the back of his head, and the mare's head hung to the ground.

"You're Finn MacCuhal," he bawled, bending his knee to the chief of the Fian. "And you're Conan," he said to the bald-headed, cross-eyed camp-master, "because you couldn't look like that and be anybody else except Conan."

"Your business, lout?" roared Conan.

"It's about getting a place in your Fian," said the fellow. "That is, if I can find out what wages you pay a lad like me."

"Does a horse-boy come with you?" Finn asked.

"Horse-boy?" said the fellow. "If I had a horse-boy he would have to get a bit out of everything I get to eat. Believe you me, Finn," said he, clapping his stomach, "I have an appetite that won't let me give anything to anyone else. I'm a Fomorian, I am," said he, "and we Fomorians do without horse-boys. And as for my mare, she's a kindly beast, and I like to keep her under my own control."

With that he picked up the rope and held the mare as if he was afraid some one of the Fian was going to take her from him.

The beaters and the stalkers were standing around, holding the hounds on their leashes, all looking at the long, knobby, down-looking mare and the outlandish-looking fellow that held her. The mare wheezed and her head dropped lower.

"Who are you?" asked Finn.

"I'm known east and west and south and north as the Gruff Gillie," he said, "or, if you like, the Rough Gillie, or the Tough Gillie. I'm called that because I've notions of my own what to do and no master that I've ever had has been able to change them. And you," said he to Finn and to the rest of the Fian who were coming out of their bothies, "don't ever try to get me to do things that I don't want to do."

"Shall we take the Gruff Gillie for a camp-servant?" said Finn to the Fian who were around.

The hounds were baying and the three battalions of the Fian felt in a sporting humour as did Finn himself. "Aye, aye," they cried. "Take him for a gillie."

"Conan," ordered Finn, "take the gillie's mare to the grazing-ground. And you, O'Duivna," he said, "have your horn ready to blow for the best chase that was ever on Knockany."

Conan, abusing everyone, led the knobby, long-backed, knock-kneed mare to the grazing ground, and the Gruff Gillie, using his club for a pole vaulted about with the joy, it would seem, of getting a place with the Fian of Ireland. It was a sight that made all forget the prospect of the chase of Knockany. But one man did not forget it; he was Dermott; he stood there, the horn in his hands, impatient to blow it.

"Isn't it nice to have bald-headed Conan for my horse-boy?" shouted the gillie as he vaulted with his club.

The horses in the grazing-ground raised their heads and sniffed as the queer-looking mare was brought amongst them. It was plain they had never seen the like of her. When Conan let go of the rope she stood with her head hanging as if she were ready to die on her four legs. The fine racers and hunters belonging to the chiefs of the Fian came around her.

Then suddenly the gillie's mare shot out her hind-legs and struck a horse belonging to Caelte full on the jaws, knocking it sideways. Then screaming and kicking she tore through the others, biting this one, kicking the other. The horses of the Fian scattered all over the grazing-field. The hounds barked, the men shouted, the horses screamed, and above all the sounds was the wheezing of the Gruff Gillie's mare.

Finn shouted an order to Conan. Conan grabbed the rope and dragged the mare from the grazing-field. "May you get as knobby and as knock-kneed, Finn," said he, "for letting the man and beast stay amongst us."

"I dare you to lay a hand on my mare," bawled the gillie. "I dare you, Conan."

Conan went on the mare's back. "I'll ride her out of this," said he. But the mare lay down, Conan on her back, and not for all the kicks he gave her would she rise again.

The Fian, their hands on their knees, laughed at Conan straddling the long mare, all except Dermott who stood with the horn in his hands.

"She's used to bigger weight than yours, manikin," bawled the gillie. "If a few of the lads get on her back she'll rise quick enough."

One, and then another, of the Fian got on the mare's back. Thirteen crowded behind Conan Baldhead. Suddenly the mare scrambled to her feet, and everybody laughed louder than before to see so many on that long back, holding her mane and holding each other. She stumbled on for a bit and the sight was so comic that the stalkers and beaters and gillies of the camp laughed in the faces of the Fian.

"Well, there's one thing I won't let the Fian of Ireland do and that is make a mock of my mare," bawled the Gruff Gillie. "That's not what I came here for. I'll go away, so I will, and I'll take my mare with me. And this will be a lesson to all honest Fomorians not to hire themselves to any pack of Irish."

With the club in his hand the gillie walked away, bawling in front of his stumbling mare. He walked fast and she went a bit fast, too. He broke into a trot and she picked up to a trot, too.

"And that's all I've got from the Fian," he shouted back to them. "Mockery! Not even a meal."

"We're wasting a fine morning, Finn," said Dermott, fidgeting with the horn. All of the three battalions were on the ground now, and the hounds could hardly be held. A stag was out up there, and they knew it. But Conan was shouting from the back of the mare:

"We can't get off! Come on and stop the mare!"

The Gruff Gillie took to running, and the mare with the fourteen on her back ran, too.

As she ran she became more and more of a steed. There were no longer hollows in her sides; her head went up, and she came to look, not only a big, but a gallant and good-looking mare.

"A murrain on you, Finn," shouted Conan. "Why don't you stir yourself? Or would you have us in the next townland before you move?"

The Gruff Gillie dropped his club, put his arms to his sides, and began to run. The mare stretched out her legs and went faster and faster, the fourteen making a jig-jog on her back.

95

Conan let a great bawl out of him.

"What sort of a captain are you, Finn MacCuhal, to let your men be carried off before your eyes?"

"Rescue!" cried Finn.

"Rescue!" cried Dermott. "Rescue, rescue!" shouted the others. With Finn at their head all made off after the mare and the Gruff Gillie. Down hollow and up height the mare went, the gillie before her, the Fian after her. One of the Fian who had been standing by when the fourteen got on the mare was able to keep up with her: he was Liagan the Swift.

Finn and the others kept on, racing as they had never raced before. It was a chase they hadn't reckoned on, but it was a chase indeed. Here and there they had a glimpse of their quarry as the mare topped a hill or swam a river. No stag had ever brought them as far as the mare, and she was still going on.

But the chase could not be given up; if he left Conan and the others in the power of a wild man, a Fomorian, Finn could never hold up his head again, let alone keep the chieftainship of the Fian of Ireland. He and his followers had to keep up the chase, no matter how long, no matter how breath-depriving, no matter how heart-breaking it was.

They burst at last into the ravines of Kerry, and there was the sea before them. They gasped out something like a cheer, for the Gruff Gillie and his mare would have to halt now. But he didn't. He took hold of the rope and went into the sea. The mare with the fourteen of the Fian on her back went into the sea, too.

Liagan took hold of the mare's tail. And as swiftly as they had raced, so swiftly did the gillie and his mare swim out, fourteen on her back and one holding to her tail.

96

Willy Pogány

"We'll have to follow them," Finn said when he and his companions reached the beach. "We're sworn to rescue any of the Fian that are in danger. Take a breath now and give our shout so that Conan and the others will know that we'll be after them." As soon as their breath came back to them, the Fian on the beach gave a shout that went across the sea and maybe came to the ears of the fifteen that were on the back and at the tail of the mare that, as it was easy to see now, was an ordinary mare no more than her master was an ordinary gillie.

The next part of the adventure was Dermott O'Duivna's. The Fian cut down trees and made a raft. When that was done they made sails out of their mantles, put on board the venison they had killed, took water, and sailed across the sea. At the end of a day they made a landfall. A high cliff went up from a narrow strand. To climb it they would have to make ladders and hack out footholds. Dermott would not wait for all this to be done: the most sure-footed of the Fian he climbed the cliff and came up on a high land where there was a wood with a mountain back of it.

He went through the wood, following a path that led to a well. Above it, hanging from a branch, was a drinking-horn half covered with silver and lavishly ornamented. And the well was very clear, but so deep was its water that Dermott could not see to the bottom. It was a well that held him in wonder.

But after a while he took the horn, dipped it in the well, and drank from it.

As he did, there came a murmur from the well. Then there was a sound of branches being pulled aside and Dermott saw coming towards him a champion who had sword and shield and helmet, and whose face had a frown of anger.

"So," he said, "without my leave you take my drinking-horn and drink from my well? This is not to be borne." And as the champion came towards Dermott he drew his sword.

Dermott was amazed that a stranger should be treated in so uncourteous a fashion. All he had done was to take a drink of water from a well in a wood, and whose leave did he have to ask for that? Still, he would have liked to have shown the Champion of the Well that there was no impudent intent in what he had done. But he came towards him so furiously that there was nothing for Dermott to do but draw his own sword.

They fought for long. But for all his fierceness the Champion of the Well was not the equal in strength or swordsmanship of one of the Fian. Dermott would have overcome him, but suddenly the champion flung his sword into the well and plunged in himself. Dermott watched him sink through the water. So deep down did he go that sight of him was lost.

The next day Dermott hunted a deer in the wood. He killed it, hung the meat and made a fire. Then when he had cooked and eaten his meat he went to the well, took the drinking-horn, dipped it in and took a draught of the water.

No sooner had he done this than a murmur came from the well; there was a sound of branches being struck aside, and he saw the Champion of the Well coming towards him.

"So," he cried, "it is not enough that you should use my drinking-horn and take a draught out of my well, but you must kill my deer also!"

Dermott held up his hand in token of friendliness. But it was no use; with sword drawn the champion came on him.

Dermott drew his sword; the two fought beside the well. But the strength and skill that men of the Fian had to have were not in the Champion of the Well. Suddenly, as on the day before, he flung his sword into the well, and before Dermott could hold him, he plunged into it. And, as before, Dermott watched him sink down until he went out of sight.

He rested there. The next day Dermott cut from the hung meat, cooked it and ate. Then he went to the well wondering what adventure would befall him.

Nothing happened until he took down the drinking-horn, and, dipping it in, drank the water of the well. Then, as before, a murmur came from the well, there was a sound of one making his way through branches, and the Champion of the Well came towards him, his sword drawn.

"So," he cried, "you will not be gone from my well!"

They fought as before. Dermott, dropping his own sword, sprang to hold him when the champion flung his sword into the well. But pulling him with him the champion plunged in. Down they sank. And when his senses were leaving him, Dermott was drawn through a passage of stone that went upward and found himself in the courtyard of a fortress. Armed men were there.

"Keep this one here," the Champion of the Well said to them, "it may be that he is the only one of the Fian of Ireland that the King of Sorca has been able to bring against me." He went into the fortress then, and the men kept a watch on Dermott.

As for Finn and the men who were with him, they made ladders and hacked out footholds, they climbed the cliff and came where Dermott left tokens of his movements. They came to the well, and standing around it, they raised the Fian's shout. They waited for Dermott's coming. And then they heard a shout, and out of a cave in the mountain a single horseman came towards them.

He saluted Finn. "I will reveal myself," he said. "I am Abartach, the King of Sorca. I came to you as the Gruff Gillie so that I might draw Finn and the Fian of Ireland to my help. I am threatened by the King of Land-under-Wave who would take from me the treasures that make me supreme in Faerie—the Spear, the Stone and the Caldron."

"Why should we fight on your side against the King of Land-under-Wave?" Finn asked him.

"Bethink thee, Finn," said the one whom they had known as the Gruff Gillie. "You have heard of Sorca and you have heard of Abartach."

He had; Finn knew he had. But what had he heard of Sorca and Abartach? Who had spoken these names? His mother? Bovmall? His uncle Crimmall? Someone talking beside a fire while a child listened. A story about help or hospitality given to his father. It was enough, that memory. Finn promised Abartach his help.

The King of Sorca brought them into the cave. Then they went down through passages in the earth. After what seemed to be a day's travel they came to a fortress. There Finn and the Fian were royally entertained. A feast was given them and there was the music of harps and the chanting of poetry. But Dermott was not with them, and Finn and his companions were downcast because of that.

As for Dermott he stayed in the courtyard of the fortress, disarmed but unguarded. The men were called to form an army that was to march away. Dermott, having eaten a meal they left for him, slept.

In a dream he thought that a fair young woman came to him and stood above him. He wakened, and it was as he had dreamed.

"Take me to where your chieftain, Finn, is," she said to Dermott.

She had the three colors—the whiteness of snow, the redness of blood, the blackness of the raven that drinks the blood that has flowed upon the snow. She was noble in her stature and graceful in her movements. She told Dermott that she loved Finn because of all she had heard about him, and longed to be with him in Ireland.

She was the sister of the King of Land-under-Wave; it was with him, as Champion of the Well, that Dermott had fought. Moriah was the fair young woman's name.

Dermott told her he did not know where Finn was. Moriah knew. He was in the fortress of the King of Sorca, and she, going with him, would show Dermott how to come to his chieftain. She led him out of the fortress and along a hidden path and brought him to where the army of the King of Sorca was arrayed.

Dermott saw his comrades of the Fian of Ireland, and he saw Finn upon a hillock, looking over the lines of battle. Dermott went to him, and his chieftain was as glad to see him as if already he had won the battle. Moriah stayed where Dermott had placed her; under a rowan tree, with a ring of shields around her.

And then the army of the King of Sorca, with Finn leading it and the Fian strengthening it, went into battle with the army of the King of Land-under-Wave. The armies fought and neither yielded to the other. Dermott sought out the enemy king. They fought as they had fought beside the well, and no more this time than the other times were the strength and the swordsmanship of the King of Land-under-Wave equal to Dermott's.

Willy Pogany

Dermott's sword pierced his shield, and the king fell upon his knee. That was the end of the battle.

Lifting up their king the army of Land-under-Wave drew back. "The treasures that make the supreme King of Faerie are Abartach's, are Abartach's," they cried as they drew back.

A feast was given for the Fian by King Abartach, and Dermott brought Moriah to it and placed her beside Finn. Even if he hadn't won a victory Finn would have been happy to have one so fair and so gracious beside him.

When the harps played Moriah chanted a poem; it was a poem of her own and it was meant for Finn only. It told him how she, a maiden of Land-under-Wave, had heard of his deeds and had loved him for what she had heard of him. And it seemed as if Finn forgot he was a warrior and remembered that he was once a poet. Anyway, when the harps sounded again he chanted a poem to Moriah.

"And I will be with you in Ireland," she said to him, and her face had all happiness in it.

In the morning Finn and the Fian stood on the narrow strand and looked towards Ireland. Moriah, lifted up on shields, looked over, too.

"What wages, Finn, would you have me give you?" Abartach asked.

"I do not remember that I paid you any wages," Finn answered, "and so there is nothing due from you to me."

"Speak for yourself, Finn," said Conan sourly.

"Speak you for the Fian, Conan," said the King of Sorca. "What wage would you have me give them?"

"Bring your mare here, and let fourteen women of your kingdom get on her back, and over with them to Ireland and across it. And let your own mare (I mean your queen) hold on where Liagan held."

The fourteen who had been on the mare cheered Conan's words. Abartach smiled. "Behold your men, Finn!" he said.

Finn looked to his men and his men looked to Finn. When they turned round again they were no longer on the narrow strand but on a wide beach with the hills of Kerry before them. And Abartach was no longer beside them.

"Back to the Hill of Almu and to our own homes," Finn commanded. His arm was around Moriah. He lifted her on his shield to give her a glimpse of Ireland. And then with shouts and songs they all marched towards Finn's house on the Hill of Almu.

Next day neither Fear Benn nor Fear Calli would give heed to the stories that Colman MacAe and Ae MacColman would tell them. They knew two stories: that was enough to keep them in conversation with each other as they stood together beside the waterfall, or walked amongst the seals, or sat under the ivy of the cliff.

The storytellers, until their bodies were shrunken through the little they had to eat, stayed with the pair. Then, each resigning his hope of the ring of gold and the steed out of Britain, they went up the cliff and took the road to King Donald's stronghold. They were able to get over their disappointment, for they fell in with some of the learned, and their spirits were raised as they recalled the proceedings of the synod:

Tales of Finn and the Fian,	Proverbs, maxims of might,
Sackings, forays, courtships,	The truthful teachings of Fithal,
Tablets inscribed in Ogham,	Dark lays of the Dinnsenchas,
Satires, keen riddles.	The teachings of Cormac and Cairbry.

As for the wild men on the beach, it was known afterwards what happened to them. Fear Calli, as he stood by the waterfall one Autumn day was blown by a blast of wind under it and was drowned. Fear Benn buried him below the ivy of the cliff.

Every day after that he heard the cry of the heron, the screech of the cormorant, the call of the plover as it flies up from its nest, and he became very affrighted, and could no longer stay under Cliff Farannan nor in the glen above it.

Once more he went wandering through Ireland.

PART FOUR

Prince Suivné at Dun na Nee

O N A DAY THAT WAS the third of the anniversaries of the battle of Moy Rah, his storytellers met the King of Ireland as he was returning from a royal progress and they joined his train with others of their degree. Luckily and auspiciously they went on until they entered the stronghold of Dun na Nee.

Colman MacAe and Ae MacColman thought of Fear Benn on the beach with the other wild man. How grand it would be to see him in his own proper form, riding with his equals to Dun na Nee, with hounds, pages, and men of every art surrounding him! And then to see him within the gates with nobles and youthful lords to do him service! And afterwards to see him in the hall, in garments of silk, with comely, gentle, well-spoken women about him, and on the board before him, for his ale, wine and metheglin, cups, and goblets and buffalo-horns! And how the King would rejoice to see such a return!

Without anything to rejoice him, the King of Ireland sat in his own hall that evening. What did he think of as he sat there silently on the anniversary of the battle he had prevailed in? His storytellers thought they knew. This was Dun na Nee that he had built, and that he thought would take a place in men's minds beside King Cormac's hall in Tara. What history would future storytellers relate of Dun na Nee? There was only one history as yet. The king told it to himself, his storytellers knew, as he sat there in the hall.

They themselves would soon go across the sea, and in Alba they would tell the story of THE BANQUET OF DUN NA NEE AND THE EVENTS THAT LED TO THE BATTLE OF MOY RAH in this way:

The
Battle of Moy Rah

I T HAS BEEN SAID that it was the difference between a goose's egg served on a silver dish and a hen's egg served on a wooden one that led to the battle of Moy Rah. The difference between a goose's egg on silver which he thought was due him, and a hen's egg on wood which was offered to him, led to Congal Claen's leaving Dun na Nee in anger, led to his gathering a great army in Alba and Britain, led to his joining that army with his own Ultonians and making war on the King of Ireland.

Those, however, who are deep-seeing in matters of history know there was more than the differences between two side-dishes offered at a banquet to make such enmity between a foster-son and a foster-father. For what startled the folk of Ireland was not so much the greatness of the forces engaged at Moy Rah, not the amount of destructiveness brought about by that battle, but the fact that in making war upon Donald, Congal Claen was making war upon one who was bound to him by the strongest of all ties, the tie that knits a foster-son to a foster-father, a foster-father to a foster-son.

But leaving the hidden cause of strife between the king and the prince to the revelation of seniors and historians, let us (the storytellers would say) tell of the famous banquet and what proceeded from it. King Donald had completed his stronghold of Dun na Nee. . . . So they would begin when they told the story to the princes of Alba.

He gave a banquet to celebrate the finishing of it. All the lesser kings were invited, all the distinguished professors, all the chief artisans. And the king determined that every kind of food and drink that had ever been served at a banquet in Ireland would be served at the banquet of Dun na Nee. He had his chamberlains make lists of such food and drink, and his chamberlains instructed his stewards to have such foods and drinks brought into the kitchens and the store rooms. But on the lists was one sort of food that was difficult to procure, and that was goose-eggs. It was not the season when geese are wont to lay. Nevertheless, the king's chamberlains ordered the stewards to go far and wide through the countryside and bring back a sufficient quantity for the banquet.

They went far and wide searching for them, but not one goose-egg could they find in the whole of Meath. Then, as they went along the edge of the River Boyne they saw a black-capped woman driving a flock of white-feathered and grey-feathered geese. "Let us follow this woman," they said, "and maybe we will be brought to a place where there are goose-eggs."

They turned up a laneway to a little hut; the geese went to their shelter and the woman went within. When the stewards looked into the hut they saw the woman at the quern and they saw on the middle of the floor a tub filled with goose-eggs. "Ho," they said, "we need go no further. And if we were to search the whole of Meath we could not have found in one place so many together."

They went within. "We are King Donald's stewards," they said, "and we are to take all the goose-eggs that are here for a banquet at Donald's royal dwelling."

"These eggs you must leave with me," the woman said.

But already two stewards had laid hands on the tub and had carried it out of the hut. "Who has a better claim on these than the king who is celebrating the finishing of his stronghold and palace?" they said to the woman.

"He for whom the eggs were kept," she answered. "Know that they have been gathered for a hermit that stays fasting in the middle of the River Boyne. Naught does he eat between day and dark but the goose-egg that he eats at night with watercress. And if you take the eggs away he will be without food."

"What is the want of a hermit compared with the want of a king?" the stewards answered roughly.

"He will curse those who deprived him of the only food he takes," said the woman, "and the curse of a hermit is a most destructive one."

"Curse or no curse," said the stewards, "we will go no further than your own doorstep, Dame, and we will take to the king's kitchens this tub of goose-eggs."

And saying this to the protesting woman, and then lifting up their voices in a ribald song, they went away carrying between a pair of them the tub of goose-eggs.

The guards before the ramparts of Dun na Nee saw a company approaching, two of them carrying a tub between them. They were the stewards, but the guards and the doorkeepers saw them as frightening people, with bristling hairs on their heads, with faces that looked as if they were smoke-blackened, with eyes in their heads that were white like snow. They went within. They left the tub with the king's chamberlains, and no one remembered seeing them again.

That evening, when the hermit came from the river and sat in the hut, the watercress before him, and waited for his goose-egg he was told by the woman of the hut that all had been taken for the king's banquet. Then the hermit (Erc was his name), went outside, and, turning towards Dun na Nee cursed it with a curse of the utmost destructiveness. Men say that the curse of a hermit is like the wedge a woodman drives into a tree: if there is a place wherein it may enter it will enter and bring down the tree. But if there is no such place it will fly back in the face of him who utters it; like the wedge that the woodman can find no entrance for it will knock out the eye of him who has tried to use it.

And then the storytellers would tell of Donald's past and of his contrivings.

Before he made himself King of Ireland, while he was yet king of the small territory of Tailtenn, Donald was in his garden and saw striplings going here and there. They were hostages, youths taken from king's houses in different provinces, and their presence there was a guarantee that their fathers would not oppose him. From many powerful kings, Donald had taken hostages even though he was king of that small place only.

He saw a youth standing with his hand to his face. "Why do you stand like that, son?" Donald said to him.

The youth took his hand from his face and the King of Tailtenn saw that his right eye was closed and swollen. "A bee from your hive stung me."

Then Donald took the youth by the hand and brought him to his own physician. Herbs of healing were put upon the swollen place, but the eye in the lad's head did not get better; it was put out of place, and ever afterwards the lad was called Congal Claen, Congal Wry-eye. Congal was the noblest of the hostages, a Ulidian, one who was of a line that went back to the time of Concobar and Cuchullain and who was descended from the noblest of the heroes after Cuchullain, from Conall Carnach. The old Ulidian kingdom had been subjugated and reduced, but those who owned the blood of Rury felt that they had a high place amongst the nobles of Ireland.

When Donald came to choose one of the hostages to be his foster-son he chose Congal Claen. "Two-thirds of a noble's disposition comes from the pattern that a foster-father gives him," the old sages said, and that saying shows how close foster-father and foster-son should be: the foster-son looked to the foster-father for all leadings towards proper manliness and gentleness, and the foster-father might look to see his foster-son better his own lineaments; treachery or shameful dealing could not be thought of as between them. Such were the ties between Donald and Congal Claen.

So when Donald was forced to exile himself from Ireland he permitted Congal Claen to come with him. Together the two escaped from danger, for Suivné Menn, the King of Ireland, became wroth with Donald who had not kept subordination, but had gone through Ireland making treaties and taking hostages and so putting himself on equality with the senior of the regnant family, with Suivné Menn, King of Ireland.

Into Alba the exiles went; they were well received by the king there, each for his own sake. For Donald was a king known to kings, and Congal was the grandson of the King of Alba, his mother being that king's daughter. Alba then was a prospering kingdom; the Gaels who had gone over there were prevailing over the Picts and Saxons, making the kingdom of the Scots flourish. And when Donald sat with the King of Alba there was kings's talk for Congal to listen to: how a king might make his authority stronger and stronger, winning over this one to his side, breaking another who opposed him, destroying him who might in time become dangerous.

Congal came one day to where his foster-father and his grandfather sat, and he heard his grandfather say, "You will be King of Ireland in place of your senior, Suivné Menn." And he heard his foster-father say, "I swear by the eight elemental things, by the sun and moon, dew and sea, heaven and earth, day and night, that I will be your friend and never your attacker."

The sight of the two kings speaking together made a stir in the mind of Congal Claen. He was like an eaglet that, stumbling over the edge of the nest, sees a land below. That was the land of kingship with its openings and its defenses. And this land was his own heritage in a way, for he, too, was of a great line. And he longed for the time when Donald would recognize him as such and would talk to him as he had talked to the other king, the time when he, Congal, would say, "I understand all you would do, my foster-father, and I will be your aider and abettor."

Afterwards Donald used to talk earnestly with his foster-son, telling him his plans and purposes, and the great things he would do when he became King of Ireland. He would make the King of Ulidia the King of all Ulster as he was in the time of Concobar: his foster-son, the descendant of Conall Carnach, would be that king. "But Suivné Menn, my senior, will live for many years yet," he said.

Then Donald and Congal Claen were able to return to Ireland. Donald went to his own domain. Congal Claen went away by himself: he went to Suivné Menn's seat. He came where Donald's senior was on his lawn and stabbed him with his spear, killing him. And before

Suivné Menn's people knew what had happened, Congal Claen was away where he could not be seen, nor found, nor reached.

The kingship of Ireland alternated between the northern and southern Nialian race. With the death of Suivné Menn, Donald, as head of the northern branch, came to the kingship. But he made no move to help Ulidia to become the kingdom it had been. His mind was now taken up with plans for the building of a royal stronghold and palace that would take the place of the royal seat for Tara that had been abandoned for a hundred years. And Congal's father was still living, and the time to extend the territory of Ulidia would be when Congal was inaugurated its king.

Congal stayed with his foster-father. But from his father's councillor he often had word that Donald was showing marks of friendship for the king of a territory that neighboured Ulidia, for Maelohar, the King of Oriel.

Dun na Nee was finished at last, with its great ramparts that were like Tara's, with its banquetting-hall that was planned to be like King Cormac's, and even with a bower such as Cormac had had made for his daughter Grania. Dun na Nee was finished, and the banquet that was to inaugurate it as the chief of the royal strongholds and palaces of Ireland was prepared. That very day one came to Congal with news of his father's death.

Thereupon Congal went to his foster-father and asked to be given a king's place at the banquet. Donald spoke to him in a friendly fashion but said that it would not be fitting that he should recognize him as king before the assembly of his own people had inaugurated him. Congal did not know what answer to make: he went back in silence to the one whom his father had had for councillor, to Gair Gann.

"The King of Ireland will give to Oriel the territory that should go to Ulidia," Gair Gann told him. "It is vain to believe that the posterity of Conn will aid the uprise of the posterity of Rury. Never will the kings who have inherited the policies of Tara let the province of Concobar be great again. And if we would make a kingdom that would be worthy of a descendant of Conall Carnach, it is not to the King of Ireland we should look, but to kings overseas."

"My foster-father will never betray my cause," said Congal Claen, his hand on that wried-eye of his. "And he knows what I did for him."

"It may be so," said Gair Gann, "but it is said that he is ready to give his daughter in marriage to the King of Oriel."

That word shook Congal, for he had fallen in love with Donald's daughter; his wried-eye throbbed; a pain went from it even to his heart.

At the great banquets it was customary for the King of Ireland to have the King of Ulster placed at his right shoulder and the King of Connacht at his left. The king who was recognized as having the headship of Ulster was not present in Dun na Nee. When Donald took his place on his gilded seat, the King of Connacht was brought to his left shoulder. Then, to the astonishment of the whole assembly, the King of Oriel was placed at his right shoulder. Congal Claen saw Maelohar in the place of the King of Ulster.

The attendants served the first dish of the banquet. To the notables beside Congal Claen a goose-egg on a silver dish was brought. And then, by mistake (perhaps it was through this mistake that Erc's curse took power) a hen's egg on a wooden dish was put before Congal.

This was an affront, Congal thought, an affront by the king who was ready to make Maelohar King of Ulster, and to give him his daughter, Congal's love, in marriage; an affront from the king whose elevation he had brought about by slaying the rightful King of Ireland! Congal was shaken by the rage that came over him. He rose up and left the banquetting-hall and went from Dun na Nee.

Donald sent messengers after him, but Congal repulsed them with bitter words.

Like a fugitive he went on, traveling night and day. He entered Ulidia and went to the house of his uncle, one who was of a stock who had remained outside Christianity, Cellach by name. Cellach was very old; he no longer walked; he was hard of hearing; he kept to his bed. But when he heard what had happened in Dun na Nee he drew out the sword that he kept under the bed-coverings, and he cried:

"I swear by the gods that the Ultonians swore by that if you, Congal, offer to Donald anything else but battle all the men of Ulster will not save you from the sword in my hand. I will thrust it into your heart. Battle for the posterity of Rury against the posterity of Conn! Fight for Concobar's province against upstart Tara. Cross the sea to Alba and raise armies there and join them with the Ulidians and the men of Dal Arahee who will no longer submit to Donald; come back to me when the sword I put into your hand has slain that upstart King."

The impetuous Congal Claen crossed the sea to Alba. On account of his pledges to Donald, the King would not join him, but he permitted his sons to raise armies and go over to Ireland and join with those who were ready to strive against the King of Ireland. And so Congal at the head of a great army faced his foster-father at Moy Rah.

It happened that a youth, who had been in fosterage in Donald's house at the time when Congal was there, lived near Moy Rah. His name was Cuanna.

Willy Pogány.

It had been discovered that Cuanna was an idiot; it was not fitting that an idiot should be fostered by a king, and so he was sent home. The simpleton held himself to be the foster-son of Donald. When he heard that battle was being offered to the one he deemed his foster-father he looked around and found a spear and betook himself to the field of Moy Rah. He entered the battle of the third day and found himself before Congal Claen.

And when Congal saw Cuanna he cried out, "Heavy is the malice and mighty the muster that brings idiots and madmen against me this day!"

Congal Claen had on the many-colored tunic that his foster-father had, long before, bestowed on him. Cuanna remembered the tunic and recognized him because of it. And as the leader of the many forces turned haughtily away, the idiot, pressing his foot against the rock and putting his finger on the cord of his spear, made a cast at him. The spear went into Congal's back; he staggered but went on, sword in hand.

As he cut his way towards where Donald stood, he came face to face with Maelohar. Even though he was becoming feeble from the wound that Cuanna had given him, Congal burst out into laughter. "Here," he cried, "is the warrior whose battling is of the pattern of the wonderful battle-evading feats of Donald himself!"

Maelohar engaged him sword to sword and the wounded Congal was hardly able to defend himself. Then the yellow lion on green satin, the streaked blue and white, the yellow and red, the red and green that were the banners of the Ulidians, the Britons, the Saxons, the Albans, went backwards, and Congal Claen was seen no more until he was found amongst the dead on the field of Moy Rah.

This was the story they would relate when they went over to Alba, Colman MacAe and Ae MacColman thought, and this was the story that, as they knew, King Donald pondered on as he sat in the hall that he had made to resemble King Cormac's hall in Tara.

There was a stir outside. The king, with that acuteness of hearing that belonged to the descendants of Ainmiré, distinguished voices. "What I hear," he said, "is not a young fox approaching a shepherd, nor a churl creeping up on a queen, nor a deer going into a field of rye in the middle of June, but it might be a hermit murmuring about something that has displeased him." He bade one of his attendants go and bring into the hall whoever was being held back by the doorkeepers.

They were nearly of equal wildness, the pair who were then brought into the hall of Dun na Nee. One was lean and in rags, and the other was bulky; this one had a single washed garment, but was bare of legs and feet and arms. Colman MacAe and Ae MacColman, as soon as they saw him, recognized the lean, ragged man.

"He is Suivné," they told the king.

"The other is the hermit Erc who cursed the banquet," the king told them.

Suivné, courteously albeit abashedly, acknowledged the welcome the king gave, but the hermit stood growling and frowning.

Then, in a loud rasping voice, he said:

"This one, whoever he may be, disturbs my meditations both when I stand in the middle of the River Boyne and when I retire to the hut and eat the one meal that I permit myself—a goose-egg. He disturbed me when he came to gather watercress from near where I bide in the river. He keeps disturbing me by declaring that I, Erc, am no hermit since I rest in a bed and eat a goose-egg daily. A hermit, he says, has to rest in trees and make his meal of watercress and nothing else. I have come with him before you, King of Ireland, to ask you to give a judgment establishing that I am a hermit."

Suivné, shaking his head, said, "I have told him that this is not an hour for kings' judgments."

"Why is it not?" inquired the hermit.

"It is the hour when the king entertains his friends," said the King of Ireland. "There are tables for all who come into the hall of Dun na Nee," he said to one and the other of the hardly clad men, and there was so much authority in the way he motioned them that Suivné, and even Erc, seated themselves before tables. Roast duck on a silver salver was placed before each. They ate, but each only the herbs with which the dish was garnished.

Then the harper played the music that was dear to the descendants of Ainmire. Suivné bowed his head and tears ran down his face. The hermit drummed like a bittern, his fist striking his chest.

When the harper had ended, the king said:

"I have a wish to hear stories that have to do with royal strongholds of other times. May Dun na Nee come to have as many heart-lifting stories told about it as the Tara of King Cormac."

"May it be so! May it be so!" the nobles and learned men present cried, and while Suivné fixed sad and remembering eyes upon them, and the hermit Erc frowned more and more blackly, the two storytellers went before the king's chair, and the taller of the pair, Colman MacAe, in his grave voice, told: THE KING OF IRELAND'S DAUGHTER.

The King of Ireland's Daughter

IT WAS VERY EARLY in the morning; the place was under Finn MacCuhal's court, Almu in Leinster; the people were Finn himself and two of his captains who had found him roaming around between the light and dark.

"What is the cause of this early rising of yours, Finn?" one asked him.

"He is wont to be without slumber and sweet sleep," said Finn, "who lacks a fitting wife. When that is the case a man is lonely and restless. Anyway, it has been so with me since Maignes, the daughter of Garad, died."

"What is it compels you to be without a wife or mate?" they said to him. "You had a wife before Maignes, and a wife before her again. And there is no woman or maiden on the green-sodded island of Eirinn, whom, if you turned your eyes on her, we would not bring you."

"And I," said one, "could show you a maiden who beyond everyone else would be a fitting wife for you."

"Whom have you in mind?" Finn asked.

"The daughter of the King of Ireland, Grania."

Finn became thoughtful. After a while he said, "There have been variance and distance between King Cormac and myself this while back, and if a refusal was given me by him there would be the width of the Shannon between us. Would you," he said to the two before him, "go to Tara and speak to King Cormac about the affair? If he refuses, no one need ever hear of it."

"We will go to Tara," the two said, "and you, Finn, say nothing about what we've gone for unless we are favored by King Cormac."

The two who spoke to Finn that early morning were Oisin the poet, Finn's son, and Duanach MacMorna the druid. It is not told how they fared till they reached Tara. But reach Tara they did; they were brought before King Cormac.

"There is not a king's son, a hero, nor a champion in Ireland to whom my daughter has not given a refusal of marriage," said the king when they told him of their errand. "And each and every one of them," he said, "lays the blame on me for the refusal."

It was easy to be seen that the king was troubled about the matter.

"I invite you to visit my daughter," he said, laying his hands on the shoulders of the envoys. "It is better you should hear her own words than that Finn MacCuhal should have any ill-feeling against myself."

So he brought Oisin and Duanach MacMorna into the women's quarters and into Grania's own bower with its window of blue grass. And he had Grania bring in bread and meat and wine so that they might feast and become familiar together. He himself sat on the couch beside his daughter.

"Here, O Grania," said King Cormac, "are two of the people of Finn MacCuhal. They have come to ask that you consider Finn for a husband. What answer do you want to give, my daughter?"

"If he be a fitting son-in-law for you, why should he not be a fitting husband for me?" Grania answered.

"There is no *if* about it as far as I'm concerned," said the king. To that Grania made no answer.

She had a thin strip of gold about her head and a piece of amber at her neck, and MacMorna the druid thought that, like the amber and gold, Grania was fine and rare but unreckonable in their possessions. She was tired of being with her women, he thought.

Oisin the poet took stock of Grania so that he might be able to speak of her when he went back to Almu. She was young to be in the place his own mother had been in, Oisin considered. She was younger than the other two wives Finn had had even when they were at their youngest. Her fingers with their reddened nails were long; her hands were long; she was long from ankle to knee, from knee to thigh. Her lips were red but very thin, her eyes were bright but not deep. She looked on them and looked on her father very steadily but as one who kept her own thought.

She would be a fit wife for Finn, Oisin told himself, for she was fair in her looks and knowledgable in what she said, and in every way showed the dignity of a king's daughter.

All went well; they feasted and became familiar. King Cormac looked cheerful when he appointed an evening for Finn and his people to come to a feast in Tara when, in the presence of Finn's people and the nobles and chiefs of Cormac's territory, Grania's hand would be placed in Finn's.

"I have never looked on Finn," said Grania, "which of you two is he like?"

"He should be like me," said Oisin, "seeing I'm his son."

"Yes," said Grania, "Finn has a son who has reached an age when he can be as famous as you are, Oisin."

Then Oisin and MacMorna went back to Almu in Leinster, and came into Finn's court there, and told him of the favorable reception that had been given them, and told him of Grania's looks and manners and words. Afterwards Finn announced the feast they had been invited to in Tara, and when the Fian knew what that feast was towards, they raised three shouts around their captain, Finn MacCuhal.

Now as everything wears away so the space of time between then and the time of the feast wore away, and the day come when Finn with his chosen chieftains left Almu for Tara. A joyous and colorful band, they crossed the plain of Leinster and nothing is told of them until they entered the Midcuartha, Cormac's great hall in Tara.

The King of Ireland sat in the raised part that in the shape of a bow was midway in the hall, commanding the upper and lower parts. His wife sat at his left shoulder and his daughter Grania sat at her left shoulder. Finn MacCuhal sat on the king's right shoulder and the druid MacMorna sat beside him.

Across the hall Cairbry, Cormac's son, sat with Oisin beside him. And in the body of the hall were the captains of the Fian and the nobles of Ireland, each according to his rank and his patrimony.

Without clamour or disturbance all were served.

Between those who were beside the king there was gentle discourse. Duanach MacMorna, as the feast went on, chanted for Grania the songs and verses and melodious poems of her fathers and ancestors, the lays of their home place, Cruachan, from whence the kings of Ireland had come to Tara.

After listening to these for a while, Grania said:

"What is the reason for Finn's coming to Tara this night?"

"If it is not known to you," said the druid, "do not wonder if it is not known to me."

"I desire to hear it from you."

"It is to ask for yourself as a wife and a mate that Finn has come to Tara."

"I marvel that it is not for the like of Oisin he would ask me," said Grania, "for it is fitter I should be with the like of him than be with a man as old as my father."

The druid kept silent at that, and Grania said:

"Who is the warrior who is just below Oisin's place?"

"Goll MacMorna, the active and soldierly."

"Who is that graceful man at the shoulder of Goll?"

"Caelte MacRonan."

"Who is the haughty looking warrior at MacRonan's shoulder?"

"MacLugaid who is sister's son to Finn MacCuhal."

"Who is the young warrior at the other side of Oisin? I mean the one with the ruddy cheeks and the curling black hair."

"He is Dermott, grandson of Duivna, favored of women and maidens, and a mortal whom Angus of the Brugh greatly cherishes."

"That must set O'Duivna well apart from the rest of you," said Grania. "No one else of the Fian, I think, is cherished by an immortal. Who is at Dermott's shoulder?"

"Diorruing. He is a very skilful leach."

"What a goodly company is here!" said Grania.

"But chief of all is the one at your father's shoulder."

"Ah, Finn!" said Grania. "Do not think you have to remind me of Finn."

But as if she had been reminded of him she called to her special handmaid and had her bring her the jewelled goblet that was in her bower behind the dais, her own goblet. The handmaid brought it and Grania filled it.

127

"Take the goblet to Finn first," she said to her handmaid, "and ask him to take a draught out of it, and let him know that it is sent by me." The goblet contained a drink for nine times nine men. In the liquor Grania put a cunning drug.

Finn laughed as he took a draught out of it. But soon he fell into a stupor and then into a slumber. The goblet was handed around. Cormac took the goblet and drank and he, too, fell into a slumber; so did Cormac's wife, Queen Eitche.

"Take the goblet to Cairbry and ask him to drink out of it; tell him it comes from Grania, and ask him to give the goblet to the nobles by him."

The handmaid did as Grania bade her.

After he had drunk out of it Cairbry was hardly able to pass the goblet on to those next him. All who drank out of the goblet fell into a deep slumber.

Thereupon Grania left her place and went to where Dermott was. She stood beside him and she said:

"Wilt thou receive courtship from me, O Dermott?"

"I may not," said Dermott, "seeing you are betrothed to my chieftain, Finn."

"That has not yet been," said Grania. "Wilt thou receive courtship from me, O'Duivna?"

"I will not, Grania, because thou dost not know me, having seen me only this once."

"I have seen you before, O'Duivna, and on a special occasion. It was at the hurling match between the Fian and the men of Tara when you saved the match for the Fian by breaking two goals against my brother Cairbry. Wilt thou receive courtship from me?"

128

"I will not. Finn would be humbled by that, and I am not one to humble my chieftain."

"Then," said Grania, "I lay obligations on you, obligations that bind you through the force of ancient Druidism, O'Duivna. I lay obligations on you to take me out of this house tonight before Finn MacCuhal and the King of Ireland come out of their slumber."

"Wicked are you to lay obligations of the kind upon me," Dermott cried. "And why do you lay them on me rather than on the sons of kings and high princes who are in this royal house tonight?" he added questioningly.

"Because there is no man in all Ireland I would have take me except you, Dermott O'Duivna. You and my father were watching the match that I saw through my window of blue grass. One of the champions of the Fian was stricken and the game was going against them. Then you sprang up, took the hurling-bat from one who was there, went into the game and won it for the Fian. I never gave my love to any man from that time to this but to you alone, Dermott, and I never will no matter what comes or goes."

"Oisin," said Dermott, "what can I do about the obligations that have been laid upon me?"

"It is part of your honor now to keep these obligations," Oisin said. "Go with Grania, but keep yourself well against the wiles and force of Finn."

"What counsel do you give me, Caelte?"

"I have a fitting wife, and yet I had rather than the wealth and fame of the world that it had been to me that Cormac's daughter proffered love."

"What counsel, O Diorruing, do you give?"

129

"Go with Grania though death come out of it and I come to grieve because of that."

"Is that the counsel of all of you?"

"It is," said Oisin, and all the others said it with him.

Then Dermott stretched out his hands and took farewell of Oisin and the chiefs of the Finn. It was no wonder he wept then; he was leaving that great companionship forever.

Now on the night that Finn was in Tara, it was he who kept the keys of the rampart, and so none could leave the royal precinct. Dermott looked to the dais where the king and queen, Finn and MacMorna were in slumber and to the other parts of the hall where those who had been given the goblet slept.

They would wake up, Dermott thought, and find himself and Grania in the hall, for there was no way of their getting beyond the rampart. Grania led Dermott up to the royal seat. Outside it was her own bower. They went through it and into a garden that was closed with a wicket gate.

"It is against my obligations as one of the Fian," said Dermott, "to go through the low gate."

But Grania went to the other side of the wicket and called to him.

"I know, O Grania," said Dermott heavily, "that the course you face towards is not for a king's daughter. I know not what nook or corner or distant part of Ireland I can take you to that would be safe from MacCuhal's vengeance."

"It is certain I will not come back," said Grania, "and that I will not part from you until death parts me from you."

"Then I will not tell you to come back," said Dermott. He put his hands on the staves of his two spears and rose and vaulted across the wall. He was on the grass-green ground of the plain beyond the rampart. Grania was beside him.

"Forward, O Grania," said Dermott as he folded her cloak about her. "We must be far away and well hidden by the time Finn MacCuhal takes his weapon in his hand."

They in the hall wakened in the early day and it was not long before it was disclosed to Finn and the others that Grania and Dermott had stolen away together. Finn stood looking into the goblet that held the draught Grania had sent him. Cormac and Cairbry went from the hall, but still Finn stood looking into the goblet. The women wailed for Grania gone, but Finn stayed movelessly there. The rest of the Fian gathered together and went out on the rampart, but Finn still stood, and still looked into the goblet. But at last he went outside and summoned his trackers; he bade them follow Dermott and Grania and show him the place where they were. He took his weapon then, and, giving a command to the troop of the Fian that were there, went with them after the trackers.

Dermott and Grania had gone a mile beyond Tara when Grania said:

"I am wearying, O'Duivna."

"Your father's mansion is not far behind," Dermott said. "Bethink you, Grania! I can bring you back without Finn or your father knowing that we went on this way."

"No, but do this, O'Duivna," said Grania. "Go back to where my father's horses are, their chariots beside them. Take horses and a chariot and come back to this place where I shall wait for you."

Dermott went. He yoked a chariot to a pair of horses and drove back to where he had left her. Grania had remained there. He lifted her into the chariot and drove on through the darkness, facing towards the west. The sun rose and Dermott hurried the horses on. It was full day when they came to the River Shannon. Dermott led one horse across and left the other to stray up or down the bank. The chariot he broke up and threw pieces of it into deep parts of the river. He lifted Grania up and carried her across the ford. And now they were in Connacht where there were many unknown and hidden places.

Finn's trackers, when they came to the river, had no more traces they could follow. But Finn told them he would hang them each side of the ford unless they found track again. What could they do but go up and down like hounds until they found it?

So they followed Dermott and Grania, the trackers and Finn with the troop he had with him. But Oisin took Bran, Finn's wise hound, and set her upon the track, knowing that if she came upon the pair she would warn them that pursuers were coming on them. Bran came to where Dermott and Grania were resting and put her head on Dermott's bosom.

"This is Finn's hound and the Fian are near us," he said.

Grania shook at the thought that she would be taken from Dermott and that he would be slain before her eyes. "Take warning and fly," she cried. And those two who now knew that in all the world they had only each other headed away from whence Bran came. They fled from hiding place to hiding place that day and the next day and the day after that. But though the trackers came close to them Dermott's comrades of the Fian always found ways of warning them when pursuit was gaining on them.

A day came when part of a forest they were lurking in was nearly surrounded and the trackers had sworn to Finn they would bring

132

Dermott's head to him, Caelte had his great-voiced henchman raise the Fian hunting-cry.

They slipped out of the forest and found badgers' holes that they hid in.

Finn went back to his court in Almu. But his jealousy about Grania and his hatred of Dermott did not abate. He put a ban upon Dermott as an outlaw in hiding from him and as a forest freebooter.

Then Dermott and Grania had respite from pursuit. The chieftain of a territory they came into permitted them to build a bothie and to hunt and fish and gather the wild fruit in his territory. Twelve moons they lived there.

One evening Dermott was strewing rushes and the soft tops of pine trees for a bed, and Grania was cooking salmon by a stream; they saw a shining figure in the glade and Dermott knew him for Angus, his fosterer. And when he had greeted them Angus, looking on them with grave and kindly gaze, said:

"The counsel I give you is that you flee from this place and from every place that you are known in, and in your going here and there never to go into a cave in which there is but one passage, never to go on an island that has but one channel between it and the land. Whatever place you cook your meal in, there eat it not; whatever place you eat in, there sleep not; whatever place you sleep in, there eat not on the morrow."

Angus went from them and at the first light Dermott and Grania left the place that had sheltered them. The wild deer was their meat and the water of the springs was their drink. They roamed Ireland while Dermott made a living by the strength of his hand and the temper of his sword.

As for Finn MacCuhal, he gave his counsel to one person only, to his woman-spy and tracker, Deirdu. She went up and down Ireland for him, finding out about Dermott and Grania, where they sheltered, who were their friends and unfriends. And by Deirdu he sent message to ancient enemies of his clan, men of the broken Clan Morna, who would gladly make peace with him.

Then one day when the chief battalion of the Fian stood with him at Almu they beheld a troop coming towards them.

"Our fathers were at the battle of Cnucha and the slaying of Cuhal," they said, "and now we want to make peace and obtain from Finn the places in the Fian that our fathers had."

"You must give compensation for the slaying of Cuhal," Finn answered them.

"We have no gold nor silver nor herds of cattle to give, Finn."

"Ask no compensation of them," said Oisin to his father. "Their fathers fell at Cnucha, and that should be compensation enough for the slaying of your father."

"It seems to me," said Finn, "that if anyone should slay me it would be an easy matter to satisfy my son in the matter of compensation. But for all that, none shall come into the Fian without giving me compensation."

"What compensation would you have us make, Finn?" asked the leader of the troop.

"I ask the head of a warrior," said Finn.

"I will give you good counsel," said Oisin, speaking to the troop whose fathers had been at the battle of Cnucha, "return to where you were reared and do not ask peace of Finn as long as you live. It is no light matter to get for Finn what he will ask of you. Return."

134

"Nay," said the leader of those dull-witted men, "our hearts are set on joining the Fian, and we will make the compensation that Finn asks of us."

When no one was beside them Finn told them what compensation he wanted from them: the head of Dermott O'Duivna.

Then one day Finn saw coming towards him his woman-tracker Deirdu, her legs failing, her tongue raving, her eyes dropping out of her head, and he knew that the day of his vengeance had come. Dermott and Grania, the woman told him, had taken refuge in the Fortress of the Ancient people, and Clan Morna were closing round that ring of stones.

Forthwith Finn summoned certain battalions of the Fian and they went swiftly towards the fortress of Da Both. Clan Morna were there. They told him that the one whose head they would bring him was within the ring of standing stones and that there was a woman with him.

"Foul fall the friends of Dermott O'Duivna for his sake," said Finn.

"Dermott O'Duivna is not there," said Oisin, "and it is a mark of your envy and jealousy, Finn, to think that he would put himself in such a place."

Then Finn lifted up his voice, and cried:

"Which of us is the truth with, O Dermott, myself or Oisin?"

And the answer of Dermott came back:

"Thou didst never err in thy judgment, Finn."

And the battalion of the Fian and the troop of Clan Morna with Finn himself standing amongst them saw Dermott stand on one of the stones of the fortress; they saw him raise Grania beside him; they saw him give her three kisses while Finn stood there. Stings of jealousy went into the heart of Finn and he swore that Dermott should give his life for those kisses.

But now Dermott, his armour on, his sword in hand, came to one of the openings in the fortress. "Who is outside?" he asked.

"No foe, Dermott, for here is Oisin. Come out to us and none will dare do thee hurt or harm."

"I will not break out until I find what opening Finn himself is at."

"Caelte is here," was said to him at another opening. "Come amongst us and we will fight and die for your sake."

"No," said Dermott, "for I will not have Finn harry you because of your well doing to myself."

To the third, to the fourth, to the fifth opening Dermott went. At the sixth he was told that the Clan Morna were there.

"Unvaliant ye are, O ye of the lie and the tracking, and it is not from fear of your hand," said Dermott, "but from disgust of you I will not go out."

He went to the seventh, and when he asked who were at that opening he heard Finn MacCuhal's voice.

"Here am I with my own henchmen, and if you should come amongst us we promise to cleave your bones asunder."

"I pledge my word," said Dermott, "that the gate that you are at, O Finn, is the very gate that I shall go through."

He turned to take farewell of Grania, and he saw beside her the shining figure of Angus of the Brugh. He knew that Grania would be taken to safety. If he were not slain by Finn and his henchmen he would be with Grania again.

"I shall put my mantle over her and depart from this without the knowledge of Finn or the Fian of Ireland," Angus said.

As for Finn, he charged his troop to let Dermott take three steps towards them. But, with his hands on the staves of his spears, Dermott vaulted across the wall and beyond Finn's troop. Standing away from them, his shield before him, his sword in his hand, he said:

"There never came on thee, Finn, battle or combat, strait or extremity in my time that I would not adventure into for thy sake and the sake of the Fian. And I swear that if thou dost attack me I shall avenge myself and thou shalt not get my head at a little cost."

"Dermott has spoken truth," said Oisin, "and it is meet that you, Finn, spare him and forgive him."

"I will not," answered Finn.

Then only the troop of Clan Morna would make the attack on Dermott. The battalions of the Fian stood by, their arms on the ground. But the troop of Clan Morna were engaged against him, and rushed upon him.

Dermott, sword in hand, passed through them as a wolf through a flock of sheep.

When Finn would go into the battle, the Fian linked their shields together and held him back. Then when the Fian drew off and the troop of Clan Morna had no more battling, Finn looked on a heap of slain and saw that Dermott was not amongst them.

Deirdu who had searched the fortress came to tell him that Grania was not to be found.

Then Finn knew all he had lost: Cormac's daughter, the trust his companions had had in him, the faith in himself that he had held since the night he had saved Tara from the Goblin. So much had Grania taken from him when she had sent him the goblet to drink out of. And his heart was still unforgiving.

As for Dermott he went to the Brugh of Angus by the Boyne. Outside it two figures stood, Angus and Grania. The life of Grania almost fled through her mouth when she saw Dermott with all the marks of combat upon him. Angus washed out his wounds and gave him a new garb and brought him and Grania into his mansion.

Later Grania went back to Tara and the King of Ireland endeavored to make peace between Dermott and Finn MacCuhal. It went hard with Finn to make peace, but he knew that he could not keep up the feud with Dermott since his own Fian would not support him in it. He agreed to the terms that Dermott proffered and he lifted the ban.

These were the terms that Finn MacCuhal and King Cormac made with Dermott O'Duivna: The district which his father owned he was let have, and the district of Cos Corann was given by King Cormac as a dowry to Grania. In his own patrimony Dermott built a great house.

If the attendants had not held him in his place, Erc the Hermit would have violently interrupted Colman MacAe's recital. As soon as the story came to a close and the attendants loosened their hold on him, Erc jumped up from his seat.

"I came here expecting judgment," he cried, "and I have had to listen to an idle tale about women and about men who never made themselves any denials."

He cast the salver with the untouched duck on the floor. "Is this, or is this not, a Hall of Judgment?" he shouted.

"It is not the hour for judgment," he was told.

"Seeking judgment here," he said, "is:

Whispering to the deaf,   Rowing without a rudder,
Seeking wool on a goat,   Looking for butter in a kennel,
Putting salt on rushes,   Shooting an arrow at a pillar,
Putting a tie upon sand,   Sucking honey from the roots of yew."

And saying this he went to the door. Nobody tried to hold him, and out of the hall he went.

"It is he who has been discourteous to the king and the company," one learned man said; and another, "No malediction can be put on Dun na Nee by him."

"He will sleep on a bed tonight," said Suivné, "in a hut with the door closed. Is such a man a hermit?" And then like a youngster who knows himself reproved for talking about his own childish affairs while uncles are having speech with grandfathers and grandmothers are advising aunts, Suivné stopped.

Then he said to King Donald:

"By your kingship, by your sovereignty, by the service to which you are entitled, have your storytellers proceed."

Thereupon the King nodded to Ae MacColman who then told: THE DEATH OF DERMOTT O'DUIVNA.

The Death
of
Dermott O'Duivna

I N THE Great House he built, the house that was named
Rath Grania, Dermott O'Duivna lay. In the dark of night
he wakened out of his sleep, starting with such violence that
Grania had to hold him.

"What has come into your mind?" she asked, her arms about him.

"It seemed to me that I heard the baying of a hound."

"But it is night," said Grania.

"It is night," said Dermott, "but I heard that baying only now. I
wonder at the baying of a hound that seems hunting in the night."

But Grania quieted him, singing to him the sleep-song that she
had sung on a night of their flight from Finn:

> Sleep, although the wild-duck, deeming
> That the fox is stepping near,
> Guides her brood from out the shallows
> To the middle of the mere.

Dermott slept, but he heard again the baying of the hound; with a start
he wakened, and again Grania quieted him with her sleep-song:

> Sleep, although the linnet rustles
> From that rounded nest of hers,
> She should keep her head enfolded—
> Nothing but the ivy stirs!

He slept again, and when he wakened it was daylight. He stood on the middle of the floor as if listening for something. His own hound, Mac an Cuill, ran whimpering about the yard.

"I will go seek the hound whose voice I heard last night," Dermott said to Grania.

"I would not have you go," Grania said. "I pray you not to go anywhere today." She put her arms about him. "Do not go where I cannot see you today," she said.

But Dermott would not have her hold him. "What should I be doing in Rath Grania on a day of May when the bushes are in blossom?" was all he said.

"That is not why you go, Dermott," Grania said.

"I will be more content," he said, "when I look from the top of Ben Gulban and know what the hound was hunting in the night."

Grania knew she could not stay him when he spoke in that way. She watched him as he made ready to betake himself from Rath Grania. As he was fastening his belt she said: "I would have you arm yourself with your great sword, the Moralltach, today."

"It is too heavy," Dermott said. "I will take my smaller sword, the Begalltach."

"In that case," said Grania, "let your spear be the great one, the Gae Derg."

"What beast could I use the Gae Derg on?" answered Dermott. "I am going hunting; I will take Mac an Cuill with me on a leash."

"When if not today," said Grania, "could we talk to our household about the feast we should give for the King of Ireland and Finn and the chiefs of the Fian? Let us arrange that today, and you, Dermott, can go hunting on Ben Gulban tomorrow."

"It is well bethought of," said Dermott, "but today is a good day for hunting and tomorrow will not be a bad day to talk about the giving of a feast."

So Dermott left Rath Grania.

All alone, leading his hound and armed with his lesser sword and his lesser spear he went up the slopes of Ben Gulban. When he reached the top there was one standing there as if waiting for him, a man with a single hound beside him. The man was Finn MacCuhal.

Dermott O'Duivna did not salute him as Finn was wont to be saluted by men of the Fian. He spoke only to ask if he were holding a chase on the hill. And Finn, looking at Dermott's hound and sword and spear answered that not he, but certain captains of the Fian were holding a chase on Ben Gulban.

"They hunt the Boar of Ben Gulban," Finn told him. "They are foolish to do that. Already the boar has wounded a score of the beaters."

"I heard a hound baying in the night," said Dermott, "and that was what brought me here."

"Leave the hill to the boar and his hunters, O'Duivna," said Finn. "I do not want you to be here."

"Why should I leave the hill," Dermott answered. "I have no dread of a boar."

"You should have," said Finn, "for you are under prohibitions about hunting a boar."

"My father was cursed on account of a boar," said Dermott, "I know that."

"The curse was to fall on your father's son and on no one else, O'Duivna," Finn said. "It has been told you by me, remember."

"Even so," said Dermott, "it would be craven of me to leave the

143

hill before I had sight of the boar. Here I stay. But would you leave your hound with mine?"

Finn did not answer. He went down the side of the hill and his hound followed him, leaving Dermott a solitary man with the hound Mac an Cuill beside him. There was a tearing noise and Dermott knew that the Boar of Ben Gulban was coming up the hill, and he knew that none was in pursuit of him because there was no baying of hounds behind him. No men, no hounds were there to hem him round.

Dermott unslipped Mac an Cuill. But the hound cowered before the bristled, gnashing brute.

He slipped his finger into the string of the Gae Bwee and made a careful cast. The spear struck the boar between his little eyes. But not a single bristle was cut, not a gash or scratch was made upon him.

"Woe to him who heeds not the counsel of a good wife," said Dermott O'Duivna to himself.

He drew the Begalltach from his belt and struck the wild boar. But even then the boar pitched him so that he fell along the bristly back. Then the boar turned and crashed down the side of the hill. He rushed back and reached the summit again. There he pitched Dermott down and gored and ripped him. And Dermott lay on the ground not able to raise himself, writhing with the pain of his deep, wide wounds.

On the track of the boar came the hunters; Finn and four chiefs of the Fian with them. They found Dermott where he was lying; and Oisin and Caelte raised him up.

"What grief to see a hero torn by a pig," said Oisin. "What grief to us to see Dermott O'Duivna in this plight."

Willy Pogany

"I grieve," said Finn, "that the women of Ireland are not here to gaze on him and to see the beauty and grace they found in him spoiled by the pig's gashes."

"Finn has come," said Dermott, knowing his voice, "and it is in his power to heal me."

"It is in Finn's power to heal Dermott," said the other chiefs of the Fian.

"I am no leach," said Finn.

"It was granted to thee, Finn, by the Women of the Green Mantles," said Dermott, "that a draught of water carried in thy hands would heal a wounded man."

"It is true what Dermott says," said Oisin, Finn's son.

"I can give the draught only to such as are deserving of it from me. What would all of you have? O'Duivna is not deserving that I should bring him water in my palms," said Finn MacCuhal harshly.

"I am well deserving of it, and you know that well, Finn," said Dermott. "Whatever you might do for me would be only a repayment for what I have done for you. When your bitter enemies cast firebrands on a house you were feasting in, I was not backward in willingness to relieve you. I bade you stay within enjoying your heady drinks while I went forth and slew men and quenched the flames. You were not surly when I came back to you. If I had asked you for a drink then you would have given it to me."

"Unfaithfulness changes everything, O'Duivna," said Finn, "and the world knows that you were unfaithful to me. You bore Grania away from me in the presence of the men of Ireland."

"I do not regret that I took Grania, Finn," said Dermott, "and it has been told you by men you can believe that Cormac's daughter put me under bonds to take her away. And that is not what you should remember.

"You should bring me a drink in your palms because of your remembrance of the time when you were beleaguered in the Brugh of the Rowan Tree, and I hastened to your relief, and by my fortune and valor brought you a goblet I had taken from your beleaguerers. I gave you that goblet in token of a victory that saved you, Finn. You should remember that and not harden your heart against me. Many a valiant man has fallen by your hand and there are others who will fall. There will be reckoning for you and the Fian. Not for you do I grieve, but for Oisin and Oscar and the rest of the brave and faithful companionship. I know that you, Oisin, will be left to lament over the Fian."

Oisin said, "I will not allow you, Finn, to withhold a drink of water from Dermott O'Duivna. And I say now that if any other prince in the world should think of doing O'Duivna such treachery there should leave this hill only whoever of us had the strongest hand. Heed what I say, and bring the water in your palms without delay."

"I know not where the wells are on this mountain," said Finn.

One of the Fian said, "Nine paces from you is a well of clear water."

Finn MacCuhal went to the well and raised the full of his hands of the water.

He turned to where Dermott O'Duivna lay. But he had not gone more than four paces when he let the water slip through his hands.

When they stepped towards him angrily he went back and took his palms' full of water out of the well. But even as he turned round he thought upon Grania and let the water slip through his hands. Dermott sighed piteously when he saw that.

"We will not stand here and see such treachery done," they said,

147

and Oisin, Oscar, Caelte and Lewy's son put their spears against Finn MacCuhal. Then Finn for the third time lifted water from the well. But as Finn stood above him, his hands held out stiffly, life parted from the body of Dermott O'Duivna.

There was silence on the top of the hill until Dermott's hound, Mac an Cuill, coming back, stood above Dermott's body and bayed long and loud. Oisin and Oscar, Caelte and Lewy's son stood there, no sighs nor groans coming from them although their hearts were wrung. They looked on Dermott who had had such grace and vigour and accomplishment, and thought about by-gone days and the joyousness that had been in the Fian, the sport, the spirit, and the companionship.

Finn MacCuhal went from them and stood beside the well. And seeing him there Caelte said, "No draught can heal you, Finn, nor make you any different from what we now know you to be: a cunning man, caring for your own ends only—you that were our mainstay."

Oisin said, "Ignobly you have done, Finn, and we never can have reverence for you again."

Lewy's son said, "The strength of the Fian will go because of this, but as you, Finn, planted the acorn, bend the oak yourself."

But Oscar thought of the affection that Angus bore to Dermott, and he cried out:

"Raise, raise the cry for him, ye Danaan hosts,
For Dermott with the weapons laid across,
And place him in your green, smooth-sided Brugh:
But we will keep the sorrow of his loss."

Then the four covered Dermott with their mantles and set a guard of the Fian around him.

Then to where Finn was standing Dermott's hound, Mac an Cuill, went, and Finn put a leash on him and held him. But his own hound stayed away from Finn.

Grania was standing on the ramparts when she saw the chiefs of the Fian coming towards Rath Grania, and she recognized them: Finn, Oisin, Oscar, Caelte, and Lewy's son, and she knew that the hound that Finn led was Dermott's. A chill went through her body. "If Dermott were alive it is not Finn who would lead Mac an Cuill," she said to herself.

When they came to where she stood they told her, "Dermott is dead, slain by the Boar of Ben Gulban."

She fainted, hearing that.

And when her senses came back to her and she knew that what she had heard was true, she raised a cry that was heard at the furthest end of the stronghold, so that her women and retainers who were there came to the rampart.

Then wailing went up from his household for Dermott O'Duivna.

Still Finn held Mac an Cuill. Grania asked him to let go the hound, but Finn said, "It is little enough I recovered from Dermott O'Duivna whom I fostered and made a hero of, and this hound of his I shall keep."

Oisin went and took the leash out of Finn's hand and brought Mac an Cuill to Grania. She sent the retainers to Ben Gulban to bring the dead back to Rath Grania. But that they did not do, for Dermott's body had been taken away by Angus Og.

As for Finn MacCuhal, he went back to Almu. Gloomy indeed were the days there, for there was no longer trust between the Fian and their chieftain.

149

When another season had passed, Finn, without the knowledge of his captains and without making any farewells to them, left Almu. To Rath Grania he went. And as he was alone and unarmed he was permitted to enter.

When Grania came to where he was, Finn told her he had come to offer a peace, and, when they had grown, to give her sons a place in the Fian.

At first Grania would not listen to him. But then she listened and he told her how Dermott's sons would be looked up to in the Fian. "But who will guarantee that?" Grania asked him.

"Yourself, Grania," Finn said. "For there is no man more fit for you to marry than myself, and there is no woman in Ireland more fit to be the wife of Finn MacCuhal than you." Grania would not listen to him at first, but then she listened, and in more and more fervent words he told her how much he loved her.

A day came when the captains of the Fian saw a pair coming towards Almu, and one was Finn, and the other, when the pair came nearer, they knew for Grania. Thereupon the captains of the Fian gave three shouts of derision and mockery. Grania bent her head in shame. But Finn took her hand and led her into the great hall of Almu.

At the banquet that night Oisin said to his father, "We trow, Finn, that from this time on you will keep Grania fast."

Whatever was meant by that, Finn did keep Grania, and Grania seemed to like being kept fast by the Chieftain of the Fian. She and Finn stayed together until one of them died. And though there was no longer that spirit amongst the Fian that Oisin and Caelte remembered, they all had to stand together, for now Cormac's son, Cairbry, stirred against them.

The next day was a bountiful and auspicious one for Colman MacAe and Ae MacColman, for King Donald, in addition to awards given them for their questings for Suivné, presented each of his storytellers with a white-spotted, red-eared cow, a shirt of white linen, and a woollen cloak with a wide broach.

How long will Eiré have to wait for another with the magnanimity of the grandson of Ainmiré? In *his* days ignorance was blasted away and partial judgments discontinued so that it was possible to suppress every evil and exalt every good. And because of the goodness of the laws, the quietness of the crowds, the serenity of the seasons, the justice of the brehons, the talents of the ollaves, the genius of the poets, the skill of the physicians, the workmanship of the smiths, the craft of the carpenters, the prowess of the magnates, the open-handedness of the hostel-keepers (in those days the hostel-keepers were not niggardly), a native or an alien could go the length and breadth of Ireland and be tranquil and well-provided for in every place.

An exceptionally beautiful damsel wearing valuable ornaments could travel without being molested (if she were prepared to brave the imputations of slander) from Osglenn in the farthest part of Connacht to Carrick Owen in Leinster, and from the islet of Innisfallen in the south to the waterfall of Assaroe in the north, or even as far as the loud-sounding cliffs of Tory. Diminished indeed are the peace and plenty, the well being and security that were in Ireland in the days when Donald was king.

But to cut abruptly and unduly this panegyric of King Donald; after the stories were told in the hall of Dun na Nee, Suivné sat without moving or speaking until the attendants brought him where a bath had been prepared for him, and from that to where his bed was made.

Thereafter he remained in Dun na Nee, no longer with authority in Dal Arahee, and living under the King of Ireland's protection.

And he would have had tranquillity there, if the words that Ronan spoke before he, Suivné, went into the battle of Moy Rah, did not keep

coming back to him. Perhaps it was to have his mind taken off Ronan and his words, that Donald sent him on a private mission to the Abbot Moling. The storytellers Colman MacAe and Ae MacColman were sent with him.

But what befell Suivné at Moling's seat in Tuam Inver will be told in another part.

PART FIVE

Prince Suivné and the Abbot Moling

TUAM INVER is by a lake. The Abbot Moling, before starting work in his field (he was a noted husbandman) was walking by the lake's edge, a book in his hand. In a gentle and cheerful voice he greeted Suivné and the two storytellers, Colman MacAe and Ae MacColman, who had come to him from King Donald. His deacon was at the gate of the churchyard ringing the bell for prime.

"My own treasure is in heaven," said Moling, "but if I had a treasure on earth it would be in wisdom and poetry." Then he turned to read in his psalter.

But Suivné, seeing before him one in the habit of a monk and with a psalter in his hand, thought that a curse was about to be put upon him. With an utterance that was like a howl, he sprang upon him and threw Moling to such a distance that he lay in a furrow.

The psalter he picked up and threw far out in the lake.

It was terrible for the storytellers to see the change that came over him. He stood there groaning and trembling.

Suivné was like a man who had been struck by a blast, by the blast for which, in their noble and copious language, the Hebrews have an appropriate word for—Sabstindrus.

154

And if Colman MacAe and Ae MacColman had not laid hands on him, Suivné would have fled from Tuam Inver and into the waste and wild places. They brought him, after Moling had lifted himself from the furrow, into the oratory.

He kept saying, "The book! The book! I flung the holy book into the depths of the lake!"

Moling, after praying in the oratory, took him by the hand. He brought him to walk by the lake, the storytellers going with them.

"It is indeed a holy book, for it belonged to no less a saint than Kevin," Moling said. "But we have to preserve a holy quietude despite such happenings."

"Ronan cursed me," said Suivné.

"Ronan of Ineasclean has gone," said Moling.

"The one who cursed me, is he dead?" Suivné cried.

Moling repeated what was said about another abbot who had died, for he hoped that something as noble would be put above Ronan:

> Angus in the assembly of Heaven,
> Here is his tomb and his bed.
> Here he passed away from sight
> On a Friday to holy Heaven.
> Here in Clonenagh he was reared,
> In Clonenagh he was buried;
> In Clonenagh of the many crosses
> He began to chant his psalms.

"I know that abbots and clerics generally are not a company that makes you happy, Suivné," Moling went on. "Still, I think your storytellers could tell you about some abbot who was likeable. Does any abbot of the kind come into stories you know?" he said to the long and short men who went with them.

"There was Cairnech," said Colman MacAe.

"Ah, Cairnech—a very pleasant man," said Moling.

"It would be good to hear about Cairnech as we walk by the water."

"The story is really about a king, and the abbot is only one of the persons in it."

"But if you can make the abbot likeable, tell us the story," said Moling. "It really would do us good to hear about a helpful abbot. Do you not think so, friend Suivné?"

"I will listen to the story," said Suivné.

So as they walked by the lake of Tuam Inver, Colman MacAe told:

MAC ERCA AND THE WIZARD WOMAN.

156

Mac Erca
and
The Wizard Woman

N THE MIDDLE of Ireland there is a pillar-stone on which this verse is cut:

> SHEEN: *Dear she might have been.*
> *Not dear were her devices.*
> *No more accursed is she*
> *Though dread is in her name.*

When people asked who she was whose name had such dread in it, the storytellers told of the death of Muircertach MacErca who was King of Ireland.

He had the title of King of Tara, though his mansion was not on Tara, but at Cletech by the River Boyne and over against the green-topped mound that was the Brugh of Angus.

At the time of the happenings that led to his death, MacErca was past his prime but was still a vigorous and valiant man. He was notable for his lineage and his own prowess: he was descended from Niall who had established the high-kingship, and he had been a leader in Denmark and Scotland before he came back to be King of Ireland and head of the Clan Niall.

His wife was the daughter of the King of Connacht and his family was ungrown.

One night when he was sleeping in his mansion at Cletech, he had this dream: he was on a ship at sea and the ship foundered; then a clawed griffin swooped down and carried him to her nest in a deep-rooted tree; the nest was set on fire, and he, and the griffin that bore him to it, fell through the fiery air. It was so present to him, the feeling of burning was so strong to him, that MacErca gasped and panted as he told his dream. He told it to his foster-brother who was the son of a druid and had much of the old pagan knowledge.

"The ship you were on," the Druid's son told him, "is the ship of your kingship, MacErca. It will founder. The griffin who carries you to her nest and falls with you is a woman who shares your abode. But this part of your dream I do not understand, for your wife, Duaibsech, is a good and faithful woman; I do not know how she can be a clawed griffin in your dream."

For many days MacErca was oppressed by the memory of his dream and troubled by the explanation that his foster-brother gave of it. And then it seemed that the explanation could not be right, for MacErca's ship of state, instead of foundering, became more firmly timbered.

He was, as has been told, a descendant of Niall, descended from that great king through the elder branch. But the descendants through the younger branch, the Clan Cairbry, did not acknowledge his supremacy, and their opposition weakened MacErca's kingship. Now it was announced that the Clan Cairbry would make a treaty of peace and friendship with him. MacErca was overjoyed.

Then a day came when he went out through his wide doors to welcome the emissaries of the Clan Cairbry.

He saw a procession coming to his place. They were the emissaries with a notable personage at their head, Cairnech, the famous bishop.

"We have come," the holy bishop said, "to knit friendship between the two branches of Niall's descendants, to the end that the kingship which you hold may prosper, MacErca."

Joyfully the king brought the bishop and the nobles of Clan Cairbry into his mansion. The treaty was sworn to, and Cairnech mingled in one vessel, blood of MacErca and blood of the prince who was of Cairbry's descendants; he called down shortening of life and pains of hell on any who would in any way infringe the treaty.

A proud and glad king was MacErca when this was done. He called in the men of every art who were in his household, and they sang songs, each one praising his own art. The king's minstrel came into the hall, and he sang the praise of the mansion, saying that not Tara, nor Emain Macha, was so splendid as trophied Cletech.

Duaibsech and her children were there, and when he sat with his queen on the high chairs in the hall, MacErca thought that the mansion would be lived in by kings who were descended from him and that it would take the place in men's minds of the great places in Tara that were now abandoned by the kings of Ireland. One thing, however, troubled his contentment as candles were lighted for the feast: it was the sight of his foster-brother. When he looked at him the dream of the foundering ship and the burning nest came back to him.

But he had no memory of the dream next day when he stood upon the grass-topped Brugh of Angus and looked across the salmon-filled Boyne to his mansion at Cletech. He had gone hunting with his guests, the nobles of Clan Cairbry, but through some chance the hunt had gone on, leaving him alone on the mound. His thoughts were proud: it was as well with him as it had been with Niall, or Conn, or Ugony, those kings who were kings of Ireland indeed. As he looked towards his timbered mansion the lines of an ancient poem were in his mind:

> I have seen a palace in a fair place
> Out of which no spoils are taken,
> Fire wastes it not, hosts harry it not:
> In prosperity is that palace perpetuated.

He knew that the house praised in the poem was the house of Angus Og of the Brugh, but it pleased him to deem that the verse fitted his own great mansion. With such thoughts in his mind MacErca looked around, and behold! near where he stood was a solitary woman.

Her hair fell in clusters, and he saw a pale face with red lips. The woman's eyes were large and wild, and her body, beautifully shaped, was as slender as a child's. A green mantle fringed with gold was upon her. She was not someone who could be overlooked.

The king went and spoke to her. "Who are you, lady?" he asked.

"I am the darling of Muircertach," she answered.

That answer and the smile that went with it transported him. "Do you know us, starbright lady?" he asked her.

"I have knowledge that belongs to places more secret than this," she said, "and I know you, Muircertach, and other princes of Ireland."

"We have not heard your name," he said.

Her names were many; she chanted them as a rann; they were ill-omened—*Tempest, Blast, Soughing Wind*. It seemed as if she wanted to make herself fearful to him.

"What name shall I call you by?" he asked.

"Sheen," she told him. And that name meaning, *suddenly gathering storm*, was fearful, too.

But MacErca had fallen in love with her: he would give all he had and all he dreamed he would have, to possess her.

"Will you come with me?" he asked, putting his arms around her.

Smiling with her red lips, she said, "If you make my reward fitting."

"I will give you a hundred out of every flock and herd I have," he promised. "I will give you golden cups and rings of gold. I will give you a feast every other night in my mansion of Cletech."

"Leave me alone on the green-topped Brugh," she cried, clasping her hands. "It were better for you to do that."

He would not listen to that saying. "I will give you power over me," he said, and his voice was not like a king's voice.

"To hear you say *that,* I have come," she said. But she did not seem glad; she hung her head. "You may not gainsay your word, and your word is now given."

He was joyful; he took her hand and they went towards his mansion at Cletech. And as they went along Sheen said:

"Duaibsech, our wife and the mother of your children, must never be in my sight. Priests must never enter the house I am in."

When she spoke these words a trembling came on MacErca. But it was given, his kingly word, and could not be recalled. The woman named Sheen he brought into his mansion.

In the hall Duaibsech, his wife sat with her children, and the holy bishop, Cairnech, was there, too. Duaibsech was on a low bench, and the bishop was instructing the children.

"Your kingly word, MacErca," Sheen said to him.

And bound by his promise and his longing for the strange woman, MacErca bade his wife and children leave the mansion, and he made Cairnech, for all his protests, leave, too. Then MacErca with Sheen

161

beside him sat on the high chairs and a feast was made ready for them in the hall.

Outside there was weeping as Duaibsech and her children, under the protection of Cairnech, went on their way.

The next morning MacErca rose up more wild about the wild-eyed woman, Sheen, than he had been before. The servants went to make fires. They no sooner struck flint than the tinder lighted, they no sooner brought tinder to the wood than the fires blazed up in the mansion of Cletech. When the servants asked for a blessing on the day there were no priests there to give it. But MacErca now looked on Sheen as a goddess. He asked her to perform a wonder so that his household might forget the priests who would never be let into the place as long as she was there.

She chanted to him:

> I can make men I can make wine
> Out of clods of clay, Out of Boyne water,
>
> Forth with me,
> O king, with your household,
> And look on wonders
> I can bring forth!

She rose slowly and went out, the king and his household followed. And when she went to where there were nettles and ferns she turned round as if to ask MacErca for a word that would reprieve her.

But he said, "I have told my folk that not Cairnech nor his clerics can accomplish what you can accomplish. Show my folk your art, O starbright Sheen."

She raised her arms and chanted a spell, and two companies of men, equally gallant, equally well armed, started up from the ground. They fell on each other, and maimed and slew each other in the presence of MacErca and his household.

And those who watched the combat were carried away by it, and they would have joined in it, but, suddenly, there were only two facing each other, and these two cut each other down. Then, as men leaving a battle-ground, the king and his household left the place and went into the mansion.

The household murmured, saying, "This is not a wonder that men should look on." But Sheen silenced them, bidding them go and bring in a full cauldron of water from the Boyne. When they brought it in she uttered spells over the water.

The king's cup-bearers filled cups and passed them round, and the king and his household thought they had never tasted wine that had such flavor and strength.

The household murmured no more against her, but smiled and nodded their heads at each other. And more than before MacErca looked on Sheen as a goddess of great power.

The king's people and the king himself fell into a heavy slumber and when they awakened the next day it was as if the strength had been taken from their bodies. They all would have Sheen work another wonder.

Again she had companies of men rise up and fight each other. And this time MacErca went into the ranks of the fighters, slaughtering and wounding all before him until he could hardly hold himself upright. Then they all went back to the mansion, and the king had Sheen prepare wine for them as before, and when they had drunk it they fell into a slumber heavier than before, and they awakened up the next day weaker even than before.

From this time on MacErca thought only of the wonders Sheen could accomplish. And when the men she had called up fought, he put on his battle-dress and went into combat with them; he would work himself into such wrath that foam would be upon his mouth. And when all had fallen before him, he would go back into his mansion, drink the wine Sheen prepared, and fall into a slumber, he and his household, that would be heavier than before.

And weaker and weaker he and his household awakened every day.

One day when he was swinging his sword among the combatants that Sheen had called up, Bishop Cairnech came to him. He thrust the cross he carried before the king.

MacErca paused; he made the sign of the cross; thereupon, instead of armed men, he saw before him only stones and clods of clay.

> With Christ's mysterious cross
> Before thine eyes,
> Abate thy fury, king,
> And no more hack the clods,

the bishop chanted. Then, very wearily, MacErca sat down on the grass. The bishop sat beside him and counselled him to go no more into his mansion that now was accursed, but to go with him to Tullen where his wife and children were. But MacErca would not go with him: he saw Sheen beckoning, and he rose up and went with her into his mansion.

But when he and Sheen sat on the high chairs in the hall, his household around them, he said, "I made the sign of the cross, and

164

behold! I saw nothing but stones and clods of clay where you had caused men to rise. Your power may be a deception."

But she kissed and clung to him, and then MacErca sang to her:

> Be with me always, you,
> Lady without reproaches;
> Your bosom's lovelier
> Than churches of the clerics.

He had dreams; he dreamt of happenings in his mansion, how the candles went up in a great flare as soon as light was brought to the wicks and how the firewood blazed as soon as lighted tinder was brought near it. And wakening he said, "A form of fire has appeared to me; it would have been well if I had taken Cairnech's counsel and left this mansion."

But Sheen who was beside him said, "Sleep. Leave the guarding of your house to me." And into his heavy slumber the king sank again.

Rising in the dawn, it seemed to him that he heard shouts of warriors outside: the Clan Cairbry, he thought, breaking the treaty they had made with him, were there to battle with him for supremacy. He put on his battle-dress and went outside, sword in hand. He pursued warriors whose battle-shouts he thought he heard.

But when he looked back for his followers he saw between himself and his mansion embers and hail of fire. He thought that Sheen was within and rushed into the house to rescue her. Fire filled the doorway; the pillars of the hall were burning. He was caught in the flames. Smothered by smoke and fume MacErca died, but his body was not completely consumed, for he drowned the fire about him from the cauldron of Boyne water.

The mansion of Cletech was burned to the ground. When the brethren sent by Cairnech came to it, they found MacErca's body in the hall.

They carried it to the river and washed it.

And as they were bearing it away, Duaibsech met them. She made mournful lamentation over the body, leaning against the ancient tree of Anach Reil. A burst of blood came from her heart and she died. And her body, too, the clerics bore along.

And as they gathered at the place where they would inter the king and queen, Cairnech and those with him saw a solitary woman coming towards them. Her mantle was green with a fringe of gold upon it; her pale face was set in sadness.

And Cairnech said to her:

"Though beautiful thy looks, we know thou hast destroyed our Muircertach, the King of Tara who lies here."

She answered. "MacErca destroyed the Old Tribes of Tara, and destroyed my fatherland, and I was sent to bring destruction on him. I strove to avert it as much as was in my power to do so, for MacErca was dearer to me than my own kin." And she chanted:

> How can I live with my
> Sorrow after him,
> The King of Ireland
> And of the Western World?
>
> A kingship I have broken. . . .
> How can I bear that guilt?

Cairnech spoke to her gently and pitifully and she confessed herself. She was baptized, and she died on the day of her baptism.

Willy Pogány

The bishop and his clerics made a grave for her and covered her with earth. And they put a pillar-stone above her. And Cairnech himself made the verse that was cut on the stone:

SHEEN: *Dear she might have been.*
Not dear were her devices
Accursed no more is she,
Though dread is in her name.

A cormorant on a rock in the lake screeched. Suivné, affrighted, trembled again.

Moling, putting his hand on Suivné's shoulder, said to Ae MacColman, "If you can relate a story that will make us feel more manful as we walk by this lake you will bring a blessing on yourself."

Colman MacAe repeated a list of recitals from which his fellow-storyteller might select an appropriate tale:

The tale of Tara's estate,
The knowledge of every cantred in Ireland,
The history of the women of Ireland,
Armies, combats, hostels, spells, captures.
Death-tales, slaughters, musical compositions,
Synchronisms, the pedigree of the king,
His battles and his hardy exploits,
And, over again, the deeds of the Ultonians.

Quickly, from the last item, Ae MacColman selected the appropriate story. "Let me at this time tell," he said, "the story that has been named: THE BLEMISHED KING."

The Blemished King

 ESIDE LOCH RURY in Ulster is a pillar-stone on which is inscribed:

Fergus, Son of Leide,
Who Died Our King.

And if you ask why the men of Ulster put the end of his life and his kingship together, the storytellers relate this story for the history of King Fergus.

He and his attendant went into the Loch to bathe. Now there was a monster in Loch Rury. They knew it, but had forgotten because this monster, the Sheenach, stayed for many years below the surface.

As King Fergus and his attendant Aed swam about they felt something rushing behind them. And then they saw, coming at them with terrible swiftness, a monster with many heads. The king's head was turned as he swam to the shore; his attendant reached it first and drew him out of the water.

"I swear by my sword-hand," said the king, "that I have been at the very jaws of death."

The singing of larks was around them, they saw the blossoming bushes, and Fergus and his attendant were exultant that they had reached safety. And then Aed turned and saw King's Fergus's face.

It was twisted; his mouth was to one side and his eye was a-squint; a red mark went from his right brow to his left jaw.

So dismayed was his attendant to see such a blemish on the king that he could not speak.

And soon the royal household would be dismayed and all the men of Ulster. For it was believed that the prosperity of the land depended on the soundness and vigor of the king. He might not be infirm and remain in the kingship. He might not even suffer the loss of a limb or an eye and have the people uphold him; he might not even have a remarkable scar.

Many famous kings had had to give up their kingdom because of some accident that had only disfigured them. And here was their own king, the King of Ulster, with his face blemished terribly!

Fergus did not know that the sight of Sheenach had marked him; that was plain, for he spoke of their escape exultantly, as if he had won a victory. And Aed talked to him and drew the hood of the king's cloak across his head for the rain had come on. So now no one they might meet on the way to the royal house would know that King Fergus was blemished.

But Aed had to tell the queen and the principals of the household. He did so while the king was in his own private chamber playing with his chess-player Moel—with Moel who had been warned by Aed about the blemishment while Fergus was changing his dress.

And when Queen Ailinn and the household heard what had happened they were all distraught!

Who was to speak to him about it since he himself did not know? Who was to be the unlucky announcer of his unkinging? Queen Ailinn and Aed and the principals of the household gave and took counsel about this while the king, unwitting of what was being debated, played chess in his own fair private chamber.

Moel pondered as he played with him. He saw that the blemish was great indeed and that there was little chance that time would remove it. The unkinging of him would be as unexpected and as dire as a visitation of sickness or of famine, for the people of Ulster regarded King Fergus as an upholder of truth and a giver of just judgments. They were certain that he had many years of kingship before him for he was in the prime of manhood; it was unlikely he would be injured because famous champions guarded him—Amergin and Conna, Eirgenn and Duvatch.

As the king's chess-player made his moves he considered what might be done for King Fergus and the people of Ulster. And by the time the game was finished he had made up his mind that if the people did not disown him, Fergus should remain king in spite of his blemish.

But he must not know that his face was marked.

How he might be kept from knowing it was what Moel considered as he made the last moves on the board.

From that day, against all custom and precedent, a king with a blemish ruled in Ireland. Aed had warned the people; when he appeared at the assembly they were affrighted by his looks; but they remembered the just judgments he had given; they heard his kindly speech, and they did not disown him.

And, instructed by the chess-player, the household kept King Fergus from knowing about his blemishment. All shining things that might show him his face, all mirrors, were removed from the house; his shield was covered with leather.

The water for his bath was taken from a brown stream that his physician recommended as good for bones and joints.

No one in the royal house spoke to him about his appearance; those who were loose of tongue or unguarded in their speech were sent away.

And that was why the juggler, the buffoon, and the dwarf were no longer at the king's call. Sent away by the queen they went to live in a hut on the shore of Loch Rury. Sometimes they would hear a bellowing and would look to where the Sheenach showed herself. Then they would see a scaly, toothed, fuming, many-headed monster making a stormy commotion as she went up and down in the water.

The buffoon and the juggler would run at the sight of her, but the dwarf would stay, and stamp and scream. Then, his mouth to one side and his eye a-squint, he would go to where the others hid.

"It is not because his face is twisted that the men of Ulster should disown King Fergus," the dwarf would say, "but because he fled from the monster of Loch Rury."

And the buffoon would say:

"What's a twist to the face (he had one himself) if one has a good tongue in one's head and can keep the people in humour?"

And the juggler who had been born on the Slige Midluachra, the road to Tara, would say:

"What is it to me whether this province has prosperity or not? There are other provinces in Ireland and there are other kings beside Fergus Wry-mouth."

The dwarf would become enraged at this kind of talk, and he would say:

"They who are of the breed of jugglers and buffoons do not understand that nothing waxes except around a waxing man. But I'm of the breed of farmers and I know that crops and the king's condition go together."

"The king's condition is good," the buffoon would say, "for there's corn in the acre and milk in the churn, and any man can eat his fill of blackberries."

And, indeed, the land continued to be prosperous. The only thing that kept it from being altogether fortunate was that the people did not have the messes of eels that they were noted for. The Sheenach on the top of the loch kept eels out of their pots that year.

King Fergus attended the fairs and assemblies, and hunted the deer and wolf and boar. He came to be happier outside his royal house than inside it. For things there were not as they were wont to be. The feasts that he gave did not have the cheer that they used to have.

He told a company of ale-drinkers about his encounter with the Sheenach of Loch Rury. Instead of forgetting their ale they buried their faces in their mugs. And when they set them down again they looked like men to whom a sorrowful story has been told.

And Ailinn, his queen, was taking it on herself more and more to dispose of the household. She had sent away his juggler, his buffoon, and his dwarf, but she would not admit that she had done this. One evening as he sat at the hearth-fire beside her he thought he would speak out what was on his mind so that there would be no more disturbance of the household.

King Fergus was gloomy; Moel the chess-player had been playing this while back as if his mind were not on the board. He had even become forgetful of his place. Last evening he told his royal partner to move, not in the unassuming voice that one uses in speaking to a king, but curtly, like one telling a fisherman where to cast a line or a net. So Fergus had forbidden Moel the private chamber and had taken from him the custody of the board. And now he was without anyone to entertain him.

He could not play chess that evening; that was the fault of Moel. But he did not have his juggler, his buffoon, or his dwarf, and that was the fault of her who sat beside him at the hearth-fire. He would speak to her about this and then say no more about the matter.

But at that moment his Man-of-smoke, his fire-tender, came to draw out the stones that were heating on the hearth.

"Where do these stones go?" Fergus asked.

"To the queen's bath," the Man-of-smoke answered.

"And the king's bath?" asked Fergus. "My feet are yet unbathed."

"It is long now, my king," the Man-of-smoke said, "since this disposal of the heated stones was made. The queen's bath comes first and then the king's." In passing the Man-of-smoke let hot ashes fall on the queen's feet. Ailinn's temper rose, and she said:

"I shall have him punished for that."

"But you will not banish him," the king replied, "as you banished my juggler, my buffoon, my dwarf." And then, giving way to anger, to the Man-of-smoke he said:

"Take the stones to the king's bath."

"Do not have this done," said Queen Ailinn to him. "Remember that in this matter I have had precedence for so long that it will dishonor me before the household if precedence is withheld from me now."

"My juggler, bid him come to me."

"He is not in the house. He was loose of tongue and I could not bear his chatter."

"Then have my buffoon come."

"He has a fever and I would not have him near us."

"My dwarf, where is he?"

"You call him your dwarf," said the queen, her feet smarting from the fall of the ashes, "but he was given me by my father. I have a right to send him back to my father's to save us all from inpertinence."

King Fergus became so angry at this reply that he struck her with that staff that was by his seat. At that Queen Ailinn with mounting temper said:

"He is with a self-respecting king and not one who strikes women rather than do what is becoming to him." And then she said as she went out of the hall, "Avenge yourself on the Sheenach of Loch Rury before you strike a king's daughter by your hearth."

"What should I avenge on the Sheenach?" he asked.

"Your twisted face," she said.

"The stones are in the king's bath," said the Man-of-smoke, coming back to the hearth.

"But my face, is it twisted?" asked the king, taking hold of him.

"I cannot tell. My eyes are near blind with smoke."

"I will see for myself," cried Fergus. Then he called for his attendant.

"Bring me a mirror," he told him.

"There are no mirrors in the house, my king," said Aed.

"A piece of polished bronze."

"There is nothing polished in the house."

"A pail of clear water from the well; I command it."

There was nothing for Aed to do except to go out to the well and fetch back water in a pail. And as he went he saw the household standing around, the queen amongst them, and there was silence and sadness on them all.

Fergus saw his face and he knew it was twisted although the image was unclear to him.

"Twisted of face, I cannot be a king," he said.

When he sent for his champions next morning he commanded them to bring uncovered shields. Into each of the four shields he looked and saw a man with mouth twisted and eye a-squint with a red mark across his face from right brow to left jaw.

He went to the assembly of the men of Ulster. He put his hands before his face, and they knew that he knew he was blemished. And now they did not hail him as their king.

"Hold me your king for yet a while," said Fergus MacLeide. He called for his sword-bearer and had him hand him his special sword, the Caladbolg, and his shield. Then he mounted his royal chariot, and, his people following, drove to the shore of Loch Rury.

In a fleet of boats the men of the province went upon the Loch. These the Sheenach scattered.

Then the men were on the shore, and Fergus said to them: "Bide here and witness how your king and the monster deal with each other."

The Sheenach, her heads raised, her nostrils smelling out the men, came rushing towards where he stood.

Fergus went into the shallows bearing his sword and his shield.

The monster rushed towards him, huge-bodied, long-fanged, her tail curved in jagged array. As a wolf's teeth are bared when a club threatens, in all her heads her teeth were bared.

Fergus dashed at her and hacked her sides with his sword. He thrust his shield into an opened maw, and, in spite of its spikes and jags, leapt upon her neck.

The Sheenach lashed the water so that fish were flung amongst the men on the shore, and the clean sand from the bottom was churned to the surface of the loch. It was white with foam.

But as the king hacked with the blade that was the best in Ireland the foam was crimsoned.

Through the monster's toughened hide he struck to her heart.

The loch turned all at once to a dark red, and through the dark redness King Fergus dashed to the shore.

He stumbled out of the water and lay down, his sword beside him. He was torn and poisoned and he groaned as he lay on the shore.

"Preserve and treasure my sword," he said. "Your king has faced the monster that disfigured him, making him no-king. I would rather death than be unkinged through being misshapen. Men of Ulster, I die your king!" So Fergus died beside the water he had reddened with the Sheenach's life blood.

In tears the men of Ulster stood above him, and in tears his bard recited his eulogy. The sword Caladbolg they put into their treasure house. And on the pillar-stone they set above him they wrote:

Fergus, Son of Leide,
Who Died Our King:

Three cormorants screeched, one after the other, but Suivné did not tremble any more. The Abbot Moling blessed the storytellers for making Suivné's spirit more steady: in good accord the four made the circuit of the lake.

But when they came to where Moling had been standing when Suivné, his senses gone astray, attacked him flinging the psalter into the lake, that unfortunate man cried out, "O cleric, I am the most discontented and unhappy being in the world; slumber nor rest will not come upon my eyes since I was so evilly inclined as to drown Kevin's holy psalter. Ronan's curse is upon me, and even though he has gone to his judgment his curse will not lift from me. I will have to stay a discontented and unhappy man since no sign of salvation is given me."

He stood there, a look of great sadness on his face and with many sighs coming from him. Then, behold! An otter came out of the lake

holding something which he laid at Moling's feet. It was the psalter, and (this was a miracle indeed) not one of its pages was destroyed.

Then, seeing Moling standing by the lake, the psalter open in his hand, the otter looking up at him, a change came over Suivné. He held up his head; he gave an exclamation of relief and gladness.

The Abbot of Tuam Inver took him by the hand and led him into the refectory, the storytellers, Colman MacAe and Ae MacColman, going, too, and ordered a collation for the three of them.

His fears departed from Suivné and he lived no more as a wild man. He did not go back to Dal Arahee, however, but remained in Tuam Inver, attending vespers each night in Moling's chapel. The Abbot liked to converse with him about his wanderings and wrote down much of his history and adventures.

In Tuam Inver Suivné died. Moling himself placed the stone on Suivné's grave.

He said, "Dear was the man whose grave this is. Often we were together; happy those days! one and the other talking as we went on yonder pathway. Heart-lifting it was to me to find him, as I would when each of us came from the field, beside yonder well. It will be Suivné's Well from this time on. But dear to me is every place where that blessed madman used to be."

Moling also made a poem in memory of Suivné which is to be found in the Book of Tuam Inver.

As for the storytellers, Colman MacAe and Ae MacColman, they went over to Alba, made themselves very noted there, and came back to Ireland with Norse cloaks on them. We have reason to believe they entered the grade of landed proprietors for there is record of grants given two storytellers that would have enabled them to do so. In that case each would have title to a dwelling house of twenty seven feet, with an outhouse of seventeen feet, with kiln, barn, mill, pig-pen, calf-enclosure, and sheep-fold. For stock, each would have twenty milch cows, two bulls, six oxen for draught, twenty yard-fed hogs, four hundred forest-reared hogs, a flock of geese, and a saddle horse with an enamelled bridle. Besides their tillage fields, each would have a grazing-field on which there would be always a flock of sheep. Of each it would be required that he should have a washing-trough, bath and brewing-vat, with implements for every season, every implement unborrowed. It would be required, too, that their fires should always be alive, their candles always in candlesticks, so that, with bacon on the hook and a goose hanging beside it, a cask of ale and a churn of milk always at hand, a supply of bread from their milled grain, each might be ready to bring in off the road a prince, a bishop, a doctor, or a judge. We may leave them, we believe, in such prosperity. At any rate we know that two storytellers received from King Donald (it is in the record of his last acts) a cow for every close in Meath, a cloak for every church, and a scrupal of gold for every prince and steward.

THE END.

NOTES

Ancient Ireland and the Stories Told

WO MEDIAEVAL NARRATIVES have been used to make a story in which older tales are placed. These two are independent narratives, the second being an offshoot from the conflict that the first recounts very fully.

The first was edited and translated just a hundred years ago by John O'Donovan: it is THE BATTLE OF MATH RATH, a prose narrative that was written to glorify the descendants of King Donald who were dynasts in Ulster as late as the eleventh century. In it Donald is written up as the pattern Irish king, that is, the pattern according to the bards. His treachery as regards his senior, Suivné Menn, is not overlooked, and Congal's taunt about his wonderful, battle-evading feats is not gainsaid. But the storyteller, in spite of these acknowledgments and in spite of conventional bombast, is able to give us a favorable impression of him.

To be in the convention of the rightful king, Donald has to be an upholder of law, and the same parable is given out about him as about other famous kings: in his time a beautiful damsel wearing things of price can go from one end of Ireland to the other unattended and unmolested.

We remember that Thomas Moore in a song has a foreign knight make an interrogation:

> Are Erin's sons so good or so cold
> As not to be tempted by woman or gold?

To which the damsel replies:

> For though they love woman and golden store,
> Sir Knight, they love honor and virtue more.

But the parable was to illustrate, not the extension of personal honor or virtue, but the stability of a social order that the King of Ireland upheld through his able judgments.

In spite of the conventional dressing-up we get the impression that Donald was an interesting and rather sympathetic personage. He was troubled about Suivné's condition and was anxious to do something that would reclaim him from his wildness: we know this from the other narrative referred to, one not written to flatter Donald's race. And his relation with the young Ulidian prince, Congal, comes out as a tragic one. This particular King of Ireland must have been proud to have associated with him a youth whose ancestor had one of the leading parts in the national epos. Congal, no doubt, was impressed by the king who undertook to build another Tara. They both dreamt of restorations. But Congal's dream of turning his little Ulidian kingdom into a great Ulster state could not have been sympathized with by the descendants of those who had destroyed, in the fourth century, Emain Macha. However much the High Kings rejoiced in tales of Concobar's time, they did not want Concobar's hegemony restored in the north. The clash that brought about the battle of Moy Rah, being inevitable, was tragic.

But in the matter of Suivne's history, the present writer has drawn even more on the second narrative than on THE BATTLE OF MATH RATH. This second narrative is SUIBHNE GELT or SUIBHNE THE MADMAN. It is in prose and verse and is quite an amazing work. Ably edited and finely translated by Mr. J. G. O'Keefe, it was published in the Irish Texts' Series about thirty years ago.

With its distinctive material SUIBHNE GELT stands all by itself in mediaeval literature.

In the present writer's version the material has been very freely treated. Neither the writer of THE BATTLE OF MATH RATH nor the writer of SUIBHNE GELT intended to produce a work which could be used to hold so many of the older stories of Ireland.

THE STORIES

Oddness in the Stories

No one can read certain of the Irish stories without feeling baffled by the motification of some of their incidents: there are *prohibitions, obligations, bonds* that the heroes are subject to. These various words are attempts to translate *geasa*. Scholars have rendered this by another out-of-the-way word, by the Polynesian *tapu* which has become *taboo* in our books. But while the tapu of the South Seas were reasonable, being directed towards practical ends, the geasa seems to be arbitrary, not directed towards any end that anyone outside of mediaeval Ireland can see.

We might suppose that in Ireland the tapu got mixed with something else—*the point of honor*. All military sets develop points of honor. In the Spanish grandees and the Japanese samurai, these are fantastic to us; in a modern officers' corps they appear reasonable. Suppose that the tapu against women going in canoes became associated with the point of honor covered by the British Old School Tie and that this point of honor had taken on the sanction of the disciplinary tapu, we might then come to understand why the prohibitions, obligations, bonds became, as they do in the later Irish stories, so fantastic. But no matter how we explain them, the fact remains that motification arising out of geasa detracts from the element of predictability in conduct that is so large an ingredient in storytelling.

As tapu, there are survivals corresponding to geasa in other communities than the Irish. So tough-minded a people as Roman generals and statesmen recognized lots of geasa: one was against any public announcement in the Forum while a thunder-storm impended. That this was something besides a practical measure is shown by the way Tacitus sums up the conduct of the Emperor Galba. That sensible man made a sensible speech recommending a fit person for his colleague. But he did it while a thunder-storm impended, and Tacitus implies

184

that this was one of the things that brought Nero's successor to his gory end. In the Roman world, however, such survivals were isolated; in Ireland, as the present writer supposes, they were given a new lease of life by being tied up with the knightly *point of honor*.

The obligation that Cuchullain was under, "not to eat the flesh of a hound" is understandable as primitive *tapu*; the obligation that Dermott is under "not to enter or leave a place through a low gateway" is understandable as a knightly *point of honor*. But these two kinds of obligation are covered by the same word. Who is Grania that she can impose on Dermott obligations that, very decidedly against his will, make him break fealty to his chieftain? Can she do it because she is the daughter of the High King? Or can any woman impose obligations of some kind on a hero? It is hard to tell; we note that the later the stories, the more fantastic and uncontrolled the geasa.

The Irish Polity

In the Ireland of King Donald's time, the seventh century, there were no towns, no army, no coinage, very little commerce. In the large entity as well as in the small ones that made it up, there were strongholds, manors, farms, churches, monastic settlements, fairs, law-courts, assemblies.

We translate 'ri' by *king,* but, whether attached to the country or to some district in it, we must not read into the title a feudal or modern meaning. The Irish king was elected by the assembly of his territory from a ruling family; he was leader in battle and president of the assembly; he was judge; he was landowner. But he had no armed force; his fighting force was made up of the freemen of his state whom he could hold together only for a limited time. Congresses or assemblies were what the political and social lives of these rural people centred around. The great assemblies were held triennially, but small assemblies must have been going on all the time, for early Ireland was made up of small states, each of which had its own king and its own assembly.

When we hear of an Irish polity first, it is in the form of a pentarchy: five kingdoms which, roughly, are represented by modern provinces—the northern Ulster, the southern Munster, the eastern Leinster, the western Connacht, with the addition of central Meath which is now two counties. Later there is a heptarchy: seven kingdoms, of which Ulster, Leinster and Connacht continue to be important. They are stable, with, as in the case of the high kingship, the same ruling families in the ascendant for generations. But these are congeries of little states. The little state, the *tuath,* is the real entity.

Professor MacNeill, in his EARLY IRISH LAWS AND INSTITUTIONS, gives a clear account of this basic community, the *tuath*. There were over eighty tuatha, each about one-third the size of an average Irish county of today. The community functioned through the assembly over which the king presided: it was the parliament, the law court, the sports gathering, the fair; it had an accompaniment of music and storytelling. To have the franchise that would permit him to take part in the assembly was the pride of a man's life. A family who did not have it could hope to have it in another generation, for the franchise went with property in land and stock that could be gained, with crafts such as smithying, house-building, boat-building, chariot-making, with literary and legal professionalism, with learning in Latin and Irish, with harp-playing. In the assembly the king's main office was that of judge. The King of Ireland was, first of all, king of a *tuath;* then as king in the proper branch of the dynastic family, he was king of Ireland. We would believe that this social and political structure was a very weak one if we did not remember that it resisted two tremendous and successive pressures, the Scandinavian and then the Norman, under which other countries quickly succumbed.

Ireland in the seventh century had a national law, a national language that was being cultivated, and a learned class that spoke in terms of national language, national law and national history. These things arose out of a social unity and strengthened that social unity.

Moy Rah

But for the moment we will leave underlying conditions to speak of the episode that is the starting point of the stories, the battle of Moy Rah or Moira (*Magh Rath* in Irish). Infiltration from a small state in the north of Ireland had created a small kingdom in the country that, centuries afterwards, was named Scotland. It was then Alba. And there was an oversea mission whose leader was Colum-cille (Saint Columba) and whose centre was Iona. Iona and the Irish state in Alba were in contact, and Columba used his influence to advance this state: he solemnly inaugurated its king, Aedan, and at a synod held in Ireland he pleaded to have this oversea kingdom freed from tributes and levies to the parent state.

This had happened three reigns back from Donald's time.

The tribute was remitted but not the levies. "Their expeditions and their hosting with the men of Ireland" was the judgment given by the synod. After this the Alban or Scottish Dal Riada (it has the same name as the parent kingdom on the Irish side) was able to make more efforts to enlarge itself. And now appears Donald Brec. He was not as successful as Aedan was in enlarging his Scottish kingdom, for he was checked in his movements against the Picts and Strathclyde Britons. He was king of both the Scottish and the Irish Dal Riada, with his seat on the Scottish side.

To him came his nephew, Congal, a young king of Ulidia and Dal Arahee in the north of Ireland, with a proposal to attack the king of Ireland's home state in the north.

For two hundred years the high kingship had been held by the descendants of Niall, the Ui Neill, or, as we should write it now, the O'Neill. Unfortunately it alternated between the northern and southern branches, and this prevented the rise of a court that might have become a national centre. The attack that was to be made on the high king's home state, had it succeeded, would have destroyed the dynasty and perhaps the high kingship.

As a ruler in an unsettled kind of state Donald Brec was able to recruit men who had been trading in war—Picts, Strathclyde Britons, Saxons. He had his own levies from the Scottish and Irish Dal Riada, and his nephew's from Ulidia and Dal Arahee. So a considerable force was assembled against the king of Ireland. And Donald Brec's professional soldiers could be kept longer in the field than the levies of the freemen of the king of Ireland and his allies. Moy Rah was an Ui Neill victory; the dynasty was able to hold the high kingship for another four hundred years.

Without the high kingship, without that aid to morale, Ireland might have been broken to bits by the subsequent Scandinavian attack. And so the battle of Moy Rah had an effect on Irish history. It probably had an effect on Scottish history as well. Moy Rah ended the intervention of the oversea kingdom in Irish affairs and that may have forced its leaders (all the nobles of the Irish Dal Riada seem to have gone over to it) to make a more strenuous effort at expansion in Alba. At any rate, the kings of Dal Riada in the course of time made themselves kings of Scotland and remained in power until the time of the Norman conquest of England.

There are certain ambiguities to be taken care of at this point:

The king of Dal Riada and the king of Ireland have the same name —Donald. There seems to have been fashions in names amongst the leading families, and Donald (Domhnall, 'world ruler' or 'possessor of dominion') was a name that had vogue at the time. Another was Suivné (Suibhne which becomes the Sweeney of today). There is Suivné Menn, the high king, and the one who is called Suivné Gelt or Frenzied Suivné. He appears as king of Dal Arahee. But he could only have been king off and on, as Congal was king of Dal Arahee as well as of Ulidia. He may have been a kind of regent while Congal was in Alba.

This is convenient for the storyteller who can call Suivné, *prince* and thereby distinguish him from the many who had *king* for title.

And the place names, Dal Riada and Dal Arahee, because of their likenesses are liable to confusion: Dal Arahee was near the Irish Dal Riada but was distinct from it.

And a reader has to know that although the name *Scot* is used for an inhabitant of Alban Dal Riada, it implies no racial differences as between him and an inhabitant of Ireland. Like *Teuton* and *German*, *Scot* and *Gael* are names for a single people. The Scots were Gaels abroad. Scot was the word used by the Romans for Gaels (Saint Patrick speaks of the sons and daughters of the Scots meaning the sons and daughters of Irish kings), and when the Gaels wrote of themselves in Latin they called themselves Scots; they even brought a queen Scotia into their ancestry. All through the middle ages the Irish on the continent were known as Scots, and it was not until the thirteenth century that the northern kingdom became definitely Scotland and its people exclusively Scots.

The high or superior king (Ard-ri) was a juridical more than a political or military figure. He had no military force, no council of state, no special revenue. He presided at the great assemblies and was judge in the highest court. When historians or storytellers recommend him they speak of him as judge, or rather as the upholder of prosperity through law. In earlier times he seems to have had another kind of office.

Tara and the Sacred Kingdom

The high-kingship developed out of the kingship of Tara, the Professor Macalister has shown in TARA, A PAGAN SANCTUARY that the early kings were priest-kings of the kind we can discern in prehistoric Greece, Italy and other countries: they were representatives of the divinity who brought about agricultural increase, and their proper office was the performance of the rites that promoted fertility.

Etain who marries the king of Tara in the story of MIDIR AND ETAIN we may suppose is the bride of a ritual marriage; she is a goddess of fertility. But some conflict seems to have underlain the rituals in early

Ireland, some dramatic tension as between the sacred kings and the divine folk. Perhaps the kings had taken possession by conquest of the possessions of people who were never the divine folk. There is something that gives dramatic significance to the marriages. The brides are such memorable women that stories about them keep recurring even in Christian times and in spite of ecclesiastical censorship. The stories last indeed into our own times when they become folk stories about the *leannean shee,* the fairy sweetheart. Perhaps the substantiality and what might be called the background of these women comes from the fact that they could be thought of as having a habitation.

Near Tara were the great mounds that had been the burial chambers and temples for a Bronze Age people. There was the Brugh, or Dwelling of Angus, a divinity associated with youth and love. The divine folk lived there, having their own histories and romances, coming out from time to time into the world of mortals, bringing mortals into their world. Midir, in this same story of MIDIR AND ETAIN is a replica of Angus.

But the sacred king had to have everything about him auspicious: he had to be sound, uninjured, and of fine appearance; he had to be married and have children. It is curious, then, to find in Eterscel of THE COWHERDS' FOSTERLING a king hedged around with prohibitions that make his marriage difficult. Perhaps there were reasons that the first storytellers understood and that became so obscure to later storytellers that they left them out. Or perhaps the story is just a folk-tale of the type of SNOW WHITE AND THE DWARFS inserted into a cycle of stories about sacred kings and their divine marriages; then the prohibitions would be a device to permit Snow White to marry royalty. But if a folk-tale, it is one that has taken over elements from a sacred story about a maiden enclosed in a kind of tower like Danae's and visited by a divine lover. Her story leads up to THE DESTRUCTION OF DA DERGA'S HOSTEL, the most characteristic and brilliant of Irish sagas, but one not given in this book.

Cuchullain is the most sympathetic hero in ancient literature—more sympathetic than Achilles or Siegfried. Like Achilles he is of semi-divine parentage: though he has an Ulster chieftain for putative father, he is really the son of the sun-god, Lugh; his mother is the sister of Concobar, the king of Ulster. Like Achilles he is to die young; like Achilles he has immortal horses that prophesy his death; like Achilles a bright light comes round his head when his valor is aroused.

Cuchullain's story belongs to the Ultonian or Ulster epic-tale, the central episode of which is Cuchullain's defense of Concobar's province against the combined provinces of Ireland led by Maeve, a queen of Connacht. This epic-tale must have taken shape before the introduction of Christianity, for the heroes are pagan, the gods and goddesses who hove through it are Danaan deities. The central district is Emain Macha, or Armagh, in the north.

Saint Patrick made Emain Macha his metropolis. Writing probably began then, and the stories that had their location in Emain Macha were, no doubt, the first secular pieces that were written down.

As written hero-tales, the Ultonian had a great prestige; this meant that in spite of their fierce provincialism they had an all-Ireland circulation: Cuchullain, who had held back the warriors of all the other provinces, was made a national hero. This was made possible through the fact that Emain Macha was no longer of any consequence and the Clann Rury to which the Ultonian heroes belonged had no political or military significance: when a prince who claims descent from one of them appears he is regarded as an interesting survival. And the written epic-tale could be given circulation because the prestige of Tara and the dignity of the high king were respected. CUCHULLAIN AND THE BATTLE GODDESS is one of the fore-tales leading up to the war for the Bull of Cooley. The heroes generally have the name *hound* (*Cu* or *Con*) in their name: this was because the great wolf hound was the mightiest beast known to the ancient Irish.

The Pictish people who had kingdoms in the north of Ireland and an important kingdom in Scotland passed out of history without leaving any sure relics of their language or their traditions but their name lives in an Empire, the British, for the name Britain comes from *Pretanni,* the Picts. One thing, however, is known about them: children were named from their mothers, descent was traced through the mother, not through the father. Women must have had an outstanding place in their organization. The Gaels of Ireland would have dramatized this feminine prominence by representing the Pictish women as Amazons. They could have found like types at home, for Maeve, Cuchullain's contemporary, had all the Amazonian qualities.

But Cuchullain goes into Pictish lands to be trained by the Amazons. There, events which were to have great bearing on his after-life take place: he becomes the comrade of Fardia whom he is to fight and slay in defense of Ulster against the armies of Maeve; he becomes the father of Connla whom he is to slay unwittingly; he obtains the mysterious weapon, the Gae Bolga. The Gae Bolga could not have been the sort of spear that is told about in this story; very likely its name meant what Professor O'Rahilly states it meant—the Spear of Bolgos, that is, of a god of the lower world who was the ancestor of many Celtic peoples, the Belgae, the Firbolg.

To bring Cuchullain to his death must have taxed the ingenuity of the ancient storytellers. With his valor, his capacity and accomplishment, his immense prestige and his semi-divine origin, he is, like Achilles, all but invincible. But they solved the difficulties admirably. The prestige of being Cuchullain's slayers is divided between two heroes; his death is led up to by sorcery; his own generosity helps towards his destruction. And with his death the heroic age passes. Still, heroes are left whose stories have to be told, and a good deal has to be said about one of them, Conall Cearnach.

The storytellers have to stage Conall as a worthy successor of Cuchullain and yet show that Conall could never attain to the sort of heroism that has gone. When his death came to be told, Cuchullain had passed the stage of being a provincial and had become a national hero; he dies in defense of his own province, Ulster; his triumph is celebrated and his death mourned in Emain Macha, but his head is buried in Tara, the seat of the king of Ireland.

Tara and the Political Kingship

Conn, his son Art, his grandson Cormac, and his great-grandson Cairbry form a dynasty at Tara that, compared with such kingships as that of Eochu and Eterscel, has the look of a political kingship. This was around A.D. 200. The dynasty was an intruding one, coming from the west, from Connacht. Cormac made Tara a social as well as a political centre by building the great Hall of Assembly in which outstanding personages amongst the nobility and learned classes were entertained during the sacred festivals; he also made the lesser kings lodge their youthful princes in Tara as hostages.

Tradition has it that Cormac became a Christian 200 years before Saint Patrick's time through contact with Roman Britain.

It is possible that in Cormac's time there were influences from Roman Britain; some scholars see in Tara's famous hall a reproduction of a Roman building and in the Fian a reproduction of the Roman legion. The Hall of Assembly left ridges that can still be seen and measured. A plan of its interior has come down to us with even a list of dishes that were served to the different grades of nobility, professional classes and royal attendants. There was a bulge into the centre, and there the king, queen, and princes had their seats commanding the upper and lower parts of the hall.

The Southern Saga

According to the storytellers the Fian was a national militia who served the kings of Tara, particularly Cormac MacAirt, and were destroyed by Cormac's successor, Cairbry, at the battle of Gowra. "Their formation was probably inspired by the example of the Roman legions, and supported by the plunder of Roman provinces, Britain and Gaul, during the decay and disorders of the Empire," Professor MacNeill states in his EARLY IRISH LAWS AND INSTITUTIONS. When that period passed, the abnormal institution of standing military forces and the military profession passed likewise.

Fian means something like *vassal* the same scholar showed in another work, and suggested that the Fian were levies conscripted from a subject population. Conn, as a conqueror, might have brought such a levy with him, and it is significant that the first Fian captain is a Connacht man, Goll MacMorma.

Neither Finn nor his captains have territorial lordship; they move readily from place to place; they support themselves as would a dispossessed people in an uncrowded country by the chase; they are hunting when they are not fighting. And Finn is no aristocratic hero as Cuchullain is; he is a folk-hero, crafty as well as brave, vindictive as well as generous. His saga came to exceed in popularity that of the Cuchullain saga; it was developed in every part of Ireland as well as in Gaelic Scotland. It had the advantage over the Cuchullain saga in that it was not written down, that it had not the fixity of a text. And it had positive advantages to help towards popularity. It was not so tragic as aristocratic sagas tend to be; it had room for humour. Then Finn, unlike Cuchullain, lives to attain the prime of manhood and to become old; he has sons and grandsons; he has a more complete and many-sided life than the short-lived and singular Cuchullain. No doubt the Finn saga rose out of the folk and was developed by the folk. However, as we shall see, it acquires court features.

The story of the GRUFF GILLIE is attached to the Finn saga, but it is a high-spirited version of a theme that is in Welsh as well as in Irish storytelling, the theme of war in Fairyland with a mortal hero enticed into the other world to be an ally of one or another of the faerie princes. Apparently a single stroke by a mortal can decide the battle.

These other stories about Finn, HOW THE HARP CAME TO TARA, THE KING OF IRELAND'S DAUGHTER and THE DEATH OF DERMOTT O'DUIVRA show the court features that have been spoken of. Evidently in the southern courts there was a building up of southern material as a counterpart to the northern saga. Finn is put forward as the national hero, the guardian of the high kingship of Tara. Then the elderly Finn's passion for Grania and her elopement with the youthful Dermott reflects the elderly Concobar's passion for Deirdre and her elopement with the youthful Naisi, while Dermott with his extraordinary feats, with his protective divinity, Angus, reflects Cuchullain with his extraordinary feats and his protective divinity, Lugh.

But the main story about Dermott is romantic and sophisticated where the northern stories are heroic and simple. And one feels that the audience who heard the tale of Dermott and Grania did not believe in Angus as the audience for the earlier story believed in Lugh. This story is crucial in the Finn saga; after this episode there is dissension in the Fian; Finn has shown himself ready to put his passion for Grania above the good of the companionship; treachery shows itself in his nature; the heroic spirit of the Fian is obscured. Then the king of Ireland, Cairbry, turns on the Fian and destroys them: Oscar, Finn's grandson, the most sympathetic of the Fian, falls at the battle of Gowra; Oisin goes into Fairyland; Finn is slain, or, according to another story, disappears. As in the Arthurian companionship, a breakup comes through passion and treachery.

Tara, too, fades out of the stories. The high kingship remains, but after the time of Niall (fifth century) it alternates between the northern and southern branches of his descendants, the Tara is only now and again the seat of the kings of Ireland. Its prestige goes. A century before King Donald's time it is abandoned.

The story goes that it was condemned by clerics as a centre of idolatry. But it is more likely that Tara fell into decay because it was not kept up by royalty.

195

THE LAST TWO STORIES

And so in MAC ERCA AND THE WIZARD WOMAN we find the ancient pattern altered. The visitant from the Brugh of Angus is not brought to Tara but to a new stronghold that is still in Meath. Ecclesiastical authority bans her. But the spell that belonged to the bride from the Fairy Mounds is still so deeply felt that, at the end, that authority has to make a reconciling gesture. Sheen's story has been given a sinister cast, but because the Irish imagination has so cherished the woman who comes out of the hidden world, she cannot be condemned. Tara is deserted; the king who keeps the title of King of Tara is counselled by Christian clerics, but the woman who comes to him keeps, for the audience would not have it otherwise, something of Etain's glamour.

And the story of THE BLEMISHED KING makes us remember that, in the imaginations of the people, kings were sacred personages. The sensational, the fantastic element in the story about Fergus MacLeide for those out of whose tradition it came would have been the people's ultra-loyalty to the disfigured king. For as a representative of the powers of growth the king's appearance had to be auspicious as his soundness had to be evident. The King Fergus of this story is supposed to have lived long before the historic kings of Tara. He ruled Ulster from Emain Macha before the other Fergus, Fergus MacRoy, who was displaced by Concobar, was king. There may have been a cycle of stories about him that was absorbed into the cycle of the other Fergus. The story of his death could not be absorbed and it holds what must have been the original conception of the early Ulster kings—that of a single-minded, heroic ruler. His sword went into the Arthurian legends: the magnificent but meaningless name of Arthur's sword *Excalibur* is *Caladbolgat* some linguistic removes.

There is a famous story about the visit of the Little People, the Lepracaun, to Fergus MacLeide's court: it is most brilliant in Irish literature. The story of Fergus MacLeide's death is tied to the story of the visit of the Lepracaun, but the tie is obviously artificial.

PADRAIC COLUM

196